THE SCIENCE BOOK OF
THE HUMAN BODY

The SCIENCE BOOK of the

HUMAN BODY

By EDITH E. SPROUL, M.D.

Illustrated by KATHLEEN ELGIN

 FRANKLIN WATTS, INC., NEW YORK

Copyright 1955 by Franklin Watts, Inc.

Library of Congress Catalog Card Number: 55-5410
Printed in the United States of America
First Printing

CONTENTS

CHAPTER

1. SOME GENERAL CONSIDERATIONS. 1

2. THE CARDIOVASCULAR SYSTEM. 11

3. THE BLOOD AND LYMPH. 25

4. THE RESPIRATORY SYSTEM. 38

5. THE ALIMENTARY SYSTEM. 54

6. THE LIVER. 72

7. THE URINARY SYSTEM. 79

8. METABOLISM 89

9. THE ENDOCRINE SYSTEM. 98

10. THE MALE REPRODUCTIVE SYSTEM. 115

11. THE FEMALE REPRODUCTIVE SYSTEM. . . . 124

12. PREGNANCY 132

13. THE NERVOUS SYSTEM AND THE SPECIAL
    SENSES 143

14. THE MUSCULO-SKELETAL SYSTEM. 182

15. THE SKIN. 201

CONTENTS (CONT.)

APPENDIX

GLOSSARY   209

BIBLIOGRAPHY   *facing* 216

INDEX   217

LIST OF ILLUSTRATIONS

DIAGRAMS

FIG.

1. EPITHELIAL TISSUE.................... 2
2. SKELETAL MUSCLE TISSUE............. 3
3. DIAGRAM OF A SINGLE CELL........... 5
4. AREOLAR CONNECTIVE TISSUE.......... 8
5. FIBROUS CONNECTIVE TISSUE BETWEEN GLANDS 9
6. DIAGRAM OF THE MITRAL VALVE (OPENED AND LAID FLAT) 15
7. DIAGRAM OF THE AORTIC VALVE....... 16
8. DIAGRAM OF CIRCULATION, INDEX FINGER 18
9. DETAIL OF ARTERIES, ARTERIOLES, AND CAPILLARIES 20
10. A VEIN (PARTLY OPENED), SHOWING VALVES 21
11. THE LYMPHATIC SYSTEM OF THE SUB-CUTANEOUS TISSUE................. 23
12. RED BLOOD CELLS.................... 26
13. THE SPLEEN, AND ITS LOCATION IN THE BODY 27
14. WHITE BLOOD CELLS................. 28
15. PHAGOCYTOSIS OF BACTERIA BY NEUTRO-PHILS 30
16. BLOOD PLATELETS................... 31

17. THE EXTERNAL NOSE.................. 39

18. NASAL CAVITIES AND SINUSES........... 41

19. DIAGRAM OF THE LARYNX, SHOWING THE
    EPIGLOTTIS AND VOCAL CORDS........ 42

20. THE TRACHEA, SHOWING BRANCHING INTO
    THE BRONCHI..................... 43

21. THE LOWER TRACHEA AND BRONCHI..... 46

22. THE THORAX, LUNGS, AND PLEURA...... 47

23. LUNG ALVEOLI..................... 48

24. DIAGRAM OF A PERSON INHALING....... 50

25. DIAGRAM OF A PERSON EXHALING....... 50

26. THE PHARYNX, INDICATED BY DARK AREA. 56

27. THE ESOPHAGUS, INDICATED BY DARK AREA 57

28. THE STOMACH, INDICATED BY DARK AREA 59

29. THE SMALL INTESTINE, INDICATED BY
    DARK AREA....................... 62

30. COURSE OF THE PERITONEUM, SHOWING
    OMENTUM 63

31. THE PANCREAS, INDICATED BY DARK AREA 65

32. THE PANCREAS, WHOLE AND IN CROSS SEC-
    TION 66

33. THE LARGE INTESTINE AND APPENDIX, IN-
    DICATED BY DARK AREA............ 69

34. THE LIVER, INDICATED BY DARK AREA.... 73

35. CROSS SECTION OF A KIDNEY, SHOWING IN-
    TERNAL STRUCTURE................ 80

36. DIAGRAM OF A KIDNEY NEPHRON........ 81

37. THE URETERS, INDICATED BY DARK AREAS. 84

38. THE URINARY BLADDER, INDICATED BY
    DARK AREA....................... 85

39. CROSS SECTION OF THE PENIS........... 87

40. THE PITUITARY GLAND, INDICATED BY DARK AREA...................... 100

41. THE ADRENAL GLANDS, INDICATED BY DARK AREAS 103

42. THE THYROID GLAND................. 111

43. THE PARATHYROID GLANDS, INDICATED BY DARK AREAS..................... 113

44. THE SCROTUM...................... 116

45. A SINGLE SPERMATOZOON............. 117

46. A TESTIS AND EPIDIDYMIS, CROSS SECTION 117

47. THE VAS DEFERENS, SHOWING CURVING INTO THE BODY................... 120

48. THE PATH OF SPERMATOZOA FROM THE TESTIS TO THE EXTERIOR (SIDE VIEW OF BODY) 121

49. THE PROSTATE AND BULBO-URETHRAL GLANDS 121

50. CROSS SECTION OF THE FEMALE REPRODUCTIVE SYSTEM................... 125

51. MICROSCOPIC VIEW OF THE CORTEX OF AN OVARY, SHOWING GRAAFIAN FOLLICLES 127

52. A MATURE OVUM.................... 128

53. THE VULVA........................ 131

54. FERTILIZATION OF AN OVUM BY A SPERMATOZOON 133

55. FALLOPIAN TUBE, UTERUS, VAGINA, AND MEETING PLACE OF SPERMATOZOON AND OVUM...................... 133

56. THE EMBRYO IN THE UTERUS, SHOWING ITS POINT OF ATTACHMENT............. 135

57. THE UTERUS, CONTAINING A FETUS...... 138

58. DIAGRAM OF THE BREAST, OR MAMMARY
     GLAND 139

59. DIAGRAM OF A MOTOR NEURON........ 144

60. A NERVE CELL OF THE CEREBRAL CORTEX 145

61. DIAGRAM OF A SENSORY NEURON........ 146

62. CROSS SECTION OF A PERIPHERAL NERVE.. 147

63. DIAGRAM OF THE KNEE-JERK REFLEX.... 148

64. LENGTH AND CROSS SECTION OF THE
     SPINAL CORD...................... 151

65. SPINAL NERVES (SIDE VIEW) 153

66. UNDERSURFACE OF THE BRAIN........ 155

67. THE CEREBRUM (SIDE VIEW) 157

68. THE LACRIMAL GLAND AND DUCTS OF THE
     EYE 165

69. THE HUMAN EYE AND A CAMERA, IN CROSS
     SECTIONS 166

70. INVERTED IMAGE OF AN ARROW AS IT AP-
     PEARS ON THE RETINA OF THE EYE... 167

71. OPTIC PATHWAY—STEREOSCOPIC VISION.. 172

72. CROSS SECTION OF THE EAR, SHOWING
     ROUTE WHICH SOUND TRAVELS....... 173

73. THE MIDDLE EAR................... 174

74. THE INNER EAR................... 175

75. A SINGLE TASTE BUD................ 178

76. THE TONGUE, SHOWING AREAS OF DIFFER-
     ENT TASTE SENSATIONS............ 179

77. OLFACTORY MUCOUS MEMBRANE OF THE
     NOSE 181

78. A CROSS SECTION OF BONE (FEMUR).... 183

79. BONE CELLS........................ 184

80. BONES OF THE SKULL (FRONT) 187

81. THE JAW JOINT..................... 189

82. CROSS SECTION OF A VERTEBRA........ 190

83. THE THORACIC CAGE, SHELTERING THE
    LUNGS AND HEART................. 191

84. THE SHOULDER GIRDLE (REAR VIEW) 192

85. THE PELVIS (FRONT VIEW) 193

86. THE ACHILLES' TENDONS, INDICATED BY
    SHADED AREAS.................... 196

87. THE ARM, ELBOW EXTENDED, SHOWING BI-
    CEPS RELAXED, TRICEPS CONTRACTED. . 197

88. THE ARM, ELBOW PARTLY BENT, SHOWING
    BICEPS PARTLY RELAXED, TRICEPS PART-
    LY CONTRACTED.................... 198

89. THE ARM, ELBOW FULLY BENT, SHOWING
    BICEPS CONTRACTED, TRICEPS RELAXED 199

90. THE SKIN AND UNDERLYING CONNECTIVE
    TISSUE 202

91. HAIR FOLLICLES AND SEBACEOUS GLANDS. 204

92. SWEAT GLANDS..................... 205

LIST OF PLATES

PLATE

(BETWEEN PAGES 110 AND 111)

I. THE HEART: INTERIOR OF THE LEFT VENTRICLE

II. THE HEART

III. DIAGRAM OF THE HEART

IV. THE CIRCULATORY SYSTEM

V. THE PULMONARY CIRCULATORY SYSTEM

VI. DETAILS OF THE HEAD: EYE, TEAR DUCT, NOSE, AND SINUSES

VII. THE RESPIRATORY SYSTEM

VIII. THE ORGANS OF THE CHEST AND ABDOMEN: FIRST LAYER

IX. THE ORGANS OF THE CHEST AND ABDOMEN: SECOND AND THIRD LAYERS

X. THE ALIMENTARY SYSTEM

XI. DETAILS OF THE HEAD: MOUTH AND EAR

XII. THE GLANDS ASSOCIATED WITH THE DIGESTIVE SYSTEM

XIII. THE URINARY TRACT TO THE BLADDER

XIV. THE MALE AND FEMALE URINARY TRACTS FROM THE BLADDER

XV. THE ENDOCRINE GLANDS

XVI. THE MALE REPRODUCTIVE SYSTEM

XVII. THE FEMALE REPRODUCTIVE SYSTEM

LIST OF PLATES (CONT.)

XVIII.   FETUS AND EMBRYO IN THE UTERUS: VARIOUS STAGES

XIX.   DELIVERY OF AN INFANT

XX.   THE CENTRAL NERVOUS SYSTEM

XXI.   THE CRANIAL NERVES

XXII.   THE PERIPHERAL NERVOUS SYSTEM

XXIII.   THE BRACHIAL PLEXUS

XXIV.   THE HUMAN SKELETON

XXV.   BONES OF THE HAND AND WRIST

XXVI.   BALL AND SOCKET JOINT OF THE HIP

XXVII.   HINGE JOINTS OF THE JAW, KNEE, AND ANKLE

XXVIII.   MUSCLES IN ACTION

XXIX.   MUSCLES IN ACTION

XXX.   THE MUSCULAR SYSTEM (FRONT VIEW)

XXXI.   THE MUSCULAR SYSTEM (BACK VIEW)

XXXII.   THE SKULL

FOREWORD

In this age of science, researchers are constantly finding evidence that has led in recent years to new concepts and new theories in the field of human physiology. Our knowledge of the human body is ever becoming wider and more complex—so much so as often to confuse the lay person, who at best can hope to have only a very general awareness of how his body works.

The Science Book of the Human Body has been published to meet the need for an up-to-the-minute book based on recent scientific findings, yet written with the simplicity and clarity necessary in a work for nonprofessional readers. We believe that from it mature persons will gain new understanding of the delicate intricacies of the human body and its functioning as a marvelously constructed whole.

Dr. Edith Sproul of Columbia University in New York is well qualified to write this book. As a researcher and teacher as well as a physician, her work has kept her in touch with new developments in the field of biological research. Our thanks to her for her many months of work in the writing of this book, and to Kathleen Elgin for her painstaking care over the illustrations. Our thanks also to Dr. Charles Poser of the Neurological Institute of New York for his advice and help, particularly with Chapter 13, "The Nervous System and the Special Senses."

The Publishers

THE SCIENCE BOOK OF
THE HUMAN BODY

1

SOME
GENERAL CONSIDERATIONS

THROUGHOUT THE YEARS the scope of human knowledge has been increasingly enlarged so that today individuals with interested and inquiring minds can be the satisfied possessors of information in many fields. At the present time lay persons have some appreciation and understanding of many areas of scientific investigation and of the arts which were once regarded as the concern of only a relatively few specialists.

But many a person lacks comprehension of his own body, of the structures within it, and of the harmonious workings of its many parts. The man who understands the mechanics of his car often has little idea of what his liver is doing or even of where it is. For some the contemplation of the body other than as a whole is repugnant. Others have felt that any understanding of human anatomy and physiology is impossible except for serious students of those subjects.

In this book what we have to say of the normal living human body represents only a small part of the knowledge available in the biological field. The subject matter dealt with here has been selected and is presented for those who are not scientists but wish to have a clearer concept of the body that plays so important a role in the life of each one of them. "A little knowledge is a dangerous thing" when it is not recognized as little and when it is used where more comprehension is needed. A little well-selected knowledge, however, can help to dispel superstitions. It may answer many of the questions which arise as we give our bodies their daily care.

If we are to understand the normal body we should know what is meant by the word "normal." The parts of the body are not formed with the precision of mechanical parts on an assembly line. They develop with many opposing forces at work; and their final form, arrangement, and behavior is the product of hereditary factors and many environmental influences. No two individuals are exactly alike. The concept of the "normal" human being, then, is a composite picture of what are regarded as the most common biological findings.

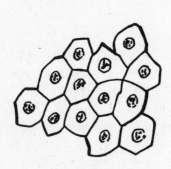

Fig. 1. Epithelial tissue.

Biological science is less exact than mathematical science. In the biological field it is often difficult to make even descriptive statements that cannot be challenged as true only in part. Knowledge changes rapidly in biology. The best that can be done is to present the state of the body as it is thought to be at the present time. Future research will undoubtedly prove some concepts to be in error.

Before the body is discussed further, several terms which are used in reference to its parts should be clarified. The ultimate living unit of the body is the cell, the nature of which is described later in this chapter. A variety of different cell types are found in every part of the body. When one type of cells having similar behavior is assembled together in large numbers, the group is called a tissue.

Throughout the body are epithelial tissues. The epithelial

cells (Fig. 1) are the ones arranged in groups or sheets without fibers between, in such a way that they form compact coverings or lining membranes. Several layers of flat epithelium cover the surface of the body and are part of the skin. Glandular epithelium, which forms secretions, lines the stomach and intestine. Epithelium arranged in cords forms the bulk of the liver. There are very many examples of different types of epithelium having various activities; they will be elaborated upon in subsequent chapters.

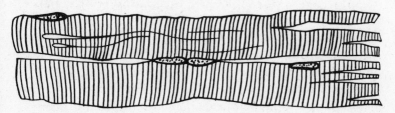

Fig. 2. Skeletal muscle tissue.

Other examples of specific tissues are the muscle tissue (Fig. 2); the bony, or osseous, tissue; the nervous tissue; and the fatty, or adipose, tissue. Their general nature is easily understood. Less commonly known types of tissue include the endothelium, which lines vascular channels such as the blood vessels; and the mesothelium, which covers the internal body cavities such as the chest and abdominal cavities.

When two or more types of tissues are grouped together in a definite pattern, and form a distinct entity which has a specific function, that structure is called an organ. The heart is an organ; so is the liver.

A group of organs and structures which are interrelated by behavior and which all contribute toward one vital function of the body is called a system. In this book we propose to describe both the structure and function or activity of the components of the human body, since true understanding depends upon correlated knowledge of all aspects of the whole. Hence information is usually presented in chapters each devoted to a specific system rather than to a single organ or to an area of the body.

In some ways the human body can be likened to a country composed of many states, the organs, in which the ultimate unit, the individual, is represented by the cell. The analogy falls down, however, when we refer to the behavior of the organs as functional systems. The respiratory system is that group of organs and structures, from nose to lungs, responsible for the entrance of air into the body and for the elimination of gases from the lungs. The reproductive system includes all organs and passages concerned essentially with the formation and development of a new individual, the child.

None of these systems can function independently, so that in a sense the respiratory or reproductive organs, for example, require the special activity of all the other systems. The respiratory system could not continue if the circulatory system failed to supply it with blood. The heart would stop beating without oxygen from the lungs. It is the aim of this book to give a simple description not only of all parts of the body and their functions, but also of the delicate interrelationships upon which they depend.

A system need not be localized in any one area of the body. In fact, its components may lie at considerable distance from one another. For example, the pituitary gland in the head is far from the other glands of the endocrine system (Pl. XV). The bone marrow belongs to the blood system, not the skeletal system, yet marrow is encased by the skeleton (Fig. 78).

The smallest living unit in the body is the cell (Fig. 3), whose name perhaps conveys the erroneous impression that it resembles the cell of a honeycomb. Actually a body cell is

4

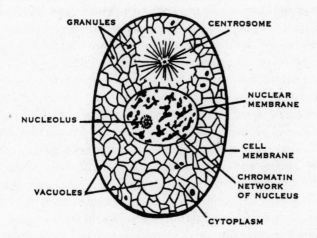

GRANULES   CENTROSOME

NUCLEAR
MEMBRANE

NUCLEOLUS

CELL
MEMBRANE

CHROMATIN
NETWORK
OF NUCLEUS

VACUOLES

CYTOPLASM

Fig. 3. Diagram of a single cell.

an entity completely enclosed in a delicate membrane that permits limited passage of fluid and materials in and out. The limiting membrane is essential to the life of the cell and ultimately to the life of the individual.

Within the cell the nucleus is the largest and most essential component which has a membrane of its own. Herein lie the nuclear genes, those units of material inherited from the original cells of the parent body. They are recognized as the unique hereditary factors which affect each individual who bears them, and they will be passed on in turn to future cell generations. These genes are held in threadlike material called chromatin, and form the chromosomes.

All the remaining material of the cell, the cytoplasm, contains very many different structures and substances, some of which cannot readily be recognized in an ordinary microscope. By technics which employ a high-speed centrifuge to isolate heavy from light particles, and by use of the electron microscope, which gives very high magnification, a variety of structures can be recognized within the cytoplasm. Some mainly contain the enzymes, a class of substances that accelerate various chemical transformations in the body; others have more of the proteins. Still others are related to the special activity of one type of cell and represent granules of secretion. Other material is nutritive.

The cells of different tissues and organs differ enough in microscopic appearance so that they can readily be recognized. They vary in shape and size, in the contour and number of nuclei, and in the character of their cytoplasmic materials. Important for recognizing them is their appearance in the group, and their relationship to each other by which they form glands or cords or interlacing fibers.

Cells can be cultivated in special media apart from the body, and if properly cared for they can reproduce themselves indefinitely. Even in such cultures many of their unique characteristics persist and their pattern of growth is individual.

Throughout the life of the body many cells are dying and are being replaced as a result of the division of young forms in each organ. Cell division is usually accomplished by the process of mitosis. In mitosis the chromatin material of the nucleus separates into chromosomes which become aligned in the middle of the nucleus. The nuclear membrane disappears. Each chromosome splits down the middle to send equivalent nuclear material to each of the two halves of the cell. When the two sets of chromosomes have moved apart, a nuclear membrane forms again about each set, and the cytoplasm divides in half, creating two independent but similar cells where there was one before.

During the development of various cells in the human embryo, cell division does more than merely reproduce its kind exactly, however. If it did not, we would never form different organs with distinct characteristics. Reproduction of cells is to some extent an unequal division in which some daughter cells differ or become "differentiated." There are two aspects of differentiation. A more highly differentiated cell takes on special characteristics of appearance and function, but it has lost its ability to grow into a variety of cell types. A poorly differentiated cell still has potential capacity for development into various cell types, but it lacks special functional abilities.

Both types—the highly differentiated functioning cells and the poorly differentiated replacement cells—are generally present in an organ. An exception is the brain, where nerve cells are developed during embryonic existence but are not replaced as they degenerate during our lifetime. The skeletal muscles and the muscle of the heart are also limited to very slight cell growth in the sense of reproduction. They can, of course, grow or increase in size by taking additional materials into the existing cells, but the number of cells will not increase.

In all organs and tissues there is a far greater abundance of functioning cells than are required for adequate performance, and there is a strong tendency to maintain this superfluous supply. If a large segment of liver is removed or damaged, the remaining healthy cells rapidly reproduce themselves to make up for the loss. If one kidney is taken out, the other becomes enlarged. Loss of nerve cells, however, is a permanent deprivation compensated for only if other nerve cells can assume some of the functions of those destroyed.

As the various organs develop in the human embryo it is obvious that a process other than multiplication and differentiation of cells is taking place. This process is "organization," by which we mean the formation of structures of a definite pattern. Organization cannot occur by growth of specialized cells alone; it requires the fibers of connective tissue as supporting framework. If kidney cells are cultivated in a tissue culture outside of the body, they grow in sheets but will not form tubules as they do in the body. If certain connective-tissue cells are added, however, the kidney cells can "organize" structures.

We recognize the essential nature of connective tissue from its name. It is present in nearly all parts of the body, forming capsules, valves, ligaments, and tendons in all the organs and in the tissues which surround individual functioning structures. Connective tissue varies greatly in character, from a loose meshwork (Fig. 4) which seems to be forming a cushion between organs to hard tough cords such as muscle tendons.

Three different types of fibers or strands mainly comprise the connective tissue. The finest ones are called reticulin fibers (Fig. 5). They form an intricate network throughout all organs and are often the main supporting structure. Heavier fibers are composed of collagen. They form the surrounding capsules of organs, and strong framework. Elastic fibers formed of elastin are found especially in tissues which

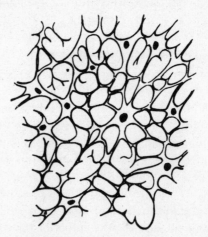

Fig. 4. Areolar connective tissue.

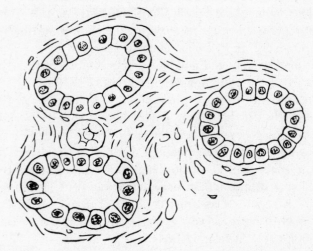

Fig. 5. Fibrous connective tissue between glands.

are subjected to expansion and contraction. They are present in blood-vessel walls, in the lungs, and in the skin.

The fibers are related in some manner to connective-tissue cells: fibroblasts and fibrocytes. We do not know exactly how the fiber is formed, but we can observe that it does form readily and in considerable quantity when an injury has occurred which leaves a gap in the tissue. These fibers are the stuff of the scar tissue which can grow in any part of the body.

Among the connective-tissue fibers, and filling in the tissue spaces throughout the body, is a mucuslike fluid called the ground substance. This varies in character in different locations and at different times according to the passage through it of materials from the cells and from the blood.

Connective tissue and ground substance were once regarded as inert supports which, beyond the supportive function, were of little interest. In recent years, however, it has been recognized that the connective tissues are the seat of alterations in many so-called allergic conditions, and more attention has been directed toward their nature and behavior. The discovery of hydrocortisone, a secretion of the adrenal gland, has brought to light the profound effect of the adrenal on the state of the connective tissues.

The story of the repair processes and regeneration of tissues in the body can be simply completed. If a few functioning cells are lost, they will usually grow back along the original framework. If the framework is injured or lost, scar tissue fills the space. But if a whole highly organized structure like a kidney or a limb is lost, none will grow back in the human body. These structures are composed of tissue too intricately organized to be replaced by the highly differentiated cells of the completely developed body.

From the unique and highly characteristic organization of cells, tissues, organs, and systems is formed the human body, whose interrelating components are discussed in the chapters which follow.

THE CARDIOVASCULAR SYSTEM is the system of blood circulation. *Cardio* means "pertaining to the heart," and *vascular* refers to "vessels that contain fluid." Hence, by the cardiovascular system is meant the heart, the arteries, the veins, and the capillaries of the human body. All the cells of the body depend on the cardiovascular system to carry to them such vital substances as oxygen and the products of digestion, and to remove from them such waste products as carbon dioxide. The circulatory system is of first importance to the functioning of the body as a whole. For instance, hormones released into the blood stream are carried to all cells by the networks of arteries and capillaries. However, the cardiovascular system itself is regulated by the nervous and endocrine systems (see pages 98 and 143). Damage to other organs such as the kidneys, lungs, and brain noticeably affect it.

In reality there are two circulatory systems, customarily called the "greater" and the "lesser." The lesser circulatory system consists of the heart, the lungs, and their interconnecting vessels. The greater circulatory system is made up of the heart and all the vessels that supply the remainder of the body with blood. There are very distinct differences between these two systems, but in each the heart is the prime mover.

This organ is situated in the midleft portion of the chest (Pl. IX). It lies within a two-layered, thin-walled sac, the pericardium. One layer closely envelops the heart itself. The other layer is loose about it. A small amount of tissue fluid between these two smooth layers permits the beating heart to move without friction.

The Heart. Although the heart is a unit, anatomically and functionally, it can be thought of as two isolated pumps—the "right heart" and the "left heart" (Pl. II and Pl. III). Normally the only route of communication between these two parts of the heart is the lung. The right heart receives blood from the veins of the entire body and pumps it into the lung by way of the lesser circulatory system. In the lung the blood is oxygenated; that is, it is supplied with oxygen. Then it moves into the left heart. From the left heart the well-oxygenated blood is pumped into a large artery called the aorta, which distributes it to the entire body by means of the greater circulatory system.

Basically the heart is a hollow muscle which is divided into four chambers. The right heart consists of an upper chamber called an atrium (or auricle) and a lower chamber called a ventricle. Between these two chambers is a one-way valve, called the tricuspid valve. The left heart has two similar chambers, but the valve that separates its chambers is called the mitral valve.

We are all aware that the heart "beats." This beating—an unceasing rhythmic contraction and relaxation—is the unique feature of heart muscle. It may be partially explained in the following way. The heart has two fairly distinct types of cells. The majority of cells are much like those of the muscles that are attached to our bones, except that the heart muscle fibers, or cells, interconnect with one another. The other type of heart cells are found in isolated areas. They are specialized structures and are of great importance in transmitting nervous impulses. Taken all together, these specialized cells are known as the Purkinje system, after the man who first described them.

It is in one of the isolated areas of specialized heart muscle, called the sino-atrial node, that the impulse causing contraction of the heart begins. This impulse has a degree of electricity that can be measured. From the sino-atrial node the impulse spreads out over both the left and right atria. There is no specialized transmitting tissue in the atria, but the interconnecting muscle fibers relay the impulse one to another. In the area where the atria meet the ventricles another mass of specialized fibers, or a node, called the atrioventricular node, is found. This node receives the impulse crossing the atria and, after a slight pause, directs it to the major segment of the Purkinje system.

This major segment, called the bundle of His, is located midway between the left and right ventricles, and has branches that radiate into both ventricles. By these branches the ventricles receive the impulse simultaneously. As with the atrial muscles, the impulse is quickly carried to all fibers of both ventricles.

The spread of the impulse throughout the heart can be recorded by an electrocardiogram—a graphic tracing of the electric current. The time for the impulse to travel from the sino-atrial node to the entire ventricular area is but a fraction of a second. The actual contraction of the muscle of the atria and ventricles occurs in succession, after the impulse has spread through each of these two parts of the heart.

While the heart has a basic rhythmic pattern, the speeding up or slowing down of the heart rate—that is, the pulse —is under nervous and chemical control. The injection of adrenalin (epinephrine) increases the heart rate. Stimulation of the vagus nerve results in its slowing down. If the amount of blood entering the right atrium increases, the heart rate speeds up. An overactive thyroid gland or excessive administration of thyroxine also accelerates the heart rate.

The heart is a far more efficient and delicately balanced pump than any that man has devised. It functions in the following way. Blood is returned from the body to the heart by two large veins, called venous trunks. These are named the inferior vena cava and the superior vena cava (Pl. II). The inferior vena cava transports blood from the lower extremities, the abdomen, and parts of the chest. The superior vena cava collects blood from the upper extremities and the head. Each of these venous trunks empties into the right atrium. Both the left and right atria are comparatively thin-walled chambers whose musculature easily adapts to the quantity of incoming blood. Blood pours into the atria when the heart muscles are relaxed. Since the atrioventricular valves are now open, blood continues passively into the relaxed ventricles. The period of relaxation is called diastole.

At this time an impulse arises in the sino-atrial node, sweeps through the muscles of the atria, and causes the atria to contract. By this means the atria squeeze into the ventricles whatever blood remains there. To reach the right ventricle the blood must pass through the tricuspid valve. To reach the left ventricle it must pass through the mitral valve.

The wave of contraction begun in the atria travels rapidly through the ventricles, and a column of blood under great pressure is forced out of the ventricles. In the right ventricle this head of blood forces the tricuspid valve to close, and opens the pulmonary valve. The blood then enters the arteries of the lung. The blood in the left ventricle closes the mitral valve, and enters the aorta, and hence the arteries of the body. The period of contraction of both atria and ventricles is called systole, although it occurs in the form of a wave.

As diastole (relaxation) comes on again, the ejected blood

14

in the pulmonary arteries and the aorta attempts to return to the ventricles. But the backward flow of blood into the ventricles is prevented by the closing of the pulmonary and aortic valves. The cycle of diastole and systole is repeated from 65 to 90 times a minute every minute of the day and night.

If the heart is to function efficiently, it must have competent valves. Its valves, the mitral, tricuspid, aortic, and pulmonic, are not composed of muscle tissue. They are made

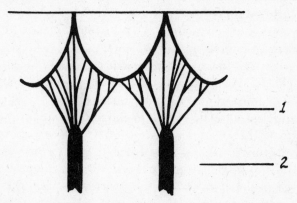

Fig. 6. Diagram of the mitral valve (opened and laid flat). 1. Chordae tendineae. 2. Papillary muscle.

of the far tougher collagenous tissue. The mitral valve (Fig. 6)—that between the left atrium and ventricle—resembles a parachute that has been cut in half. The parts that correspond to a parachute's shroud lines are called chordae tendineae. They are anchored in muscular projections (papillae) of the inner surface of the left ventricle (Pl. I). The chordae tendineae are placed in the ventricle in such a way that the two valve leaflets (which correspond to the parachute proper) can close tight over the passageway between the left atrium and ventricle. In the working of a parachute, it is the inrush of a column of air that inflates the chute. With the mitral valve, it is the inrush of ventricular blood striking the valve leaflets that moves them into position. With the impact of a column of blood the two valve leaflets swing up and meet in the midline, and the chordae tendineae act as shroud lines to keep them in position. The edges of the valve leaflets are so finely constructed and fit together so closely that the valve is watertight. The tricuspid valve, which separates the right atrium and ventricle, is constructed on the same principle. As its name implies, however, it has three valve leaflets.

The aortic and pulmonic valves are built differently from the mitral and tricuspid valves. They are like hinges. The aortic valve is situated where the aorta joins the left ventricle (Pl. I). It is constructed of cusps—three hingelike projections from the wall of the aorta (Fig. 7). When the left ventricle contracts, it sets in motion a column of blood that strikes the cusps and pushes their free ends outward against the aortic wall so that blood is free to flow into the aorta. When the ventricle relaxes, the backward pressure of the blood in the aorta swings the cusps away from the aortic wall. Now they are at right angles to the aorta and fit together to close tight the ventricular outlet, much as a dia-

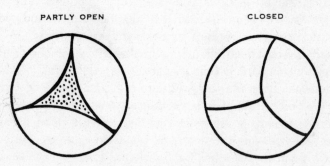

PARTLY OPEN   CLOSED

Fig. 7. Diagram of the aortic valve.

phragm would. In this way the blood in the aorta is prevented from flowing back into the ventricle. The pulmonic valve is a similar hinge attached to the right ventricle. If anything prevents the valve leaflets or cusps from moving freely or distorts their shape, they cannot function correctly as they are no longer watertight.

The muscles of the heart itself are supplied with fresh, oxygenated blood by two arteries called the left and right coronary arteries. These arteries are the first branches leaving the aorta. The openings of the coronary vessels can be seen just above the aortic valve. During diastole (relaxation) the coronary arteries fill with blood and supply the heart. All other arteries receive their greatest blood flow during systole (contraction).

There are two reasons why the coronary arteries fill during diastole. When the heart is in systole, its muscles contract and narrow the branches of the coronary arteries within it. Also, in systole the head of blood in the aorta is traveling away from the heart at considerable speed, and only small quantities enter the coronary vessels. In diastole, back pressure forces considerably more blood into the mouths of the coronary vessels.

The Circulation. As was previously stated, the heart, though a unit, can be thought of as two isolated pumps. The right heart receives venous blood from the entire body and pumps it into the lung by way of the pulmonary artery (Pl. V). The pulmonary artery is a short, quickly branching blood vessel which carries venous—unoxygenated—blood. The blood pressure in this artery is lower than that in the other arteries of the body. Blood flowing through the lung meets less resistance than does blood flowing through all the other organs of the body. So the right ventricle normally contracts with less force than does the left ventricle and is less muscular, even though it ejects the same volume of blood. The lesser con-

17

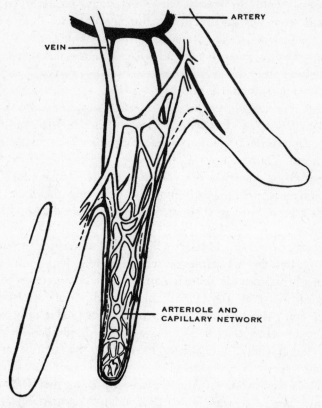

ARTERY

VEIN

ARTERIOLE AND
CAPILLARY NETWORK

Fig. 8. Diagram of circulation, index finger of the hand.

traction results in the lower pressure in the pulmonary artery.

After the blood is oxygenated in the lung it moves into the left heart by way of the pulmonary vein. The left ventricle then pumps the oxygenated blood into the aorta, which distributes it to the body (Pl. IV). Blood entering the aorta from the left ventricle is tapped by numerous arteries along the whole course of the aorta. These arteries, carrying oxy-

18

genated blood, enter the various organs and divide into smaller branches called arterioles (little arteries). The arterioles, in turn, branch and terminate in capillaries (Fig. 8). In the capillaries the oxygen in the blood is released for use by tissue cells.

Groups of capillaries then fuse to form venules which merge into veins. Venous blood, which contains much less oxygen than arterial blood does, is returned to the right ventricle by way of the inferior and superior venae cavae. This, in brief, is the course of the blood through the circulatory system. Arteries, arterioles, capillaries, and veins are built differently and function differently. Nervous, hormonal, and chemical controls integrate their individual operation, however.

As the arteries extend from the aorta into the branches and their finer ramifications, their structure changes. However, there is always an inner lining membrane composed of a single layer of cells. This lining forms a smooth surface for blood to pass over. In the aorta the outer wall is composed of loose connective tissue containing small blood vessels, nerves, and lymphatics (see page 23). The middle coat, the largest, consists of a patchwork of elastic fibrous tissue and smooth muscle. This coat gives the aorta its resiliency. The inner coat is a thin smooth lining. Blood enters the aorta under a great head of pressure during systole and distends its walls. In diastole the aortic walls spring back to their original position.

The branches of the aorta—the arteries proper—contain less elastic fibrous tissue in their middle coats and proportionately more smooth muscle (Fig. 9). The arterioles contain almost no elastic tissue; the middle coat is primarily muscular. This smooth muscle sheath can contract so as to narrow and at times entirely close the passageway of the arterioles.

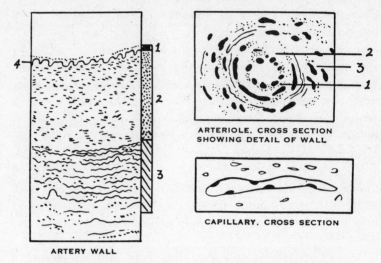

ARTERIOLE, CROSS SECTION
SHOWING DETAIL OF WALL

CAPILLARY, CROSS SECTION

ARTERY WALL

Fig. 9. Detail of arteries, arterioles, and capillaries. 1. Inner coat. 2. Muscle coat. 3. Outer wall. 4. Elastic membrane.

The capillaries are at the ends of the arterioles and have walls composed of a one-cell layer. One arteriole gives rise to a great many capillaries. Capillaries from different arterioles interconnect so as to form a capillary "bed" within a given organ or structure. Arterioles may also interconnect, but not to the extent that capillaries do. The single-celled capillary wall allows the passage of oxygen and other substances into the surrounding tissue. Moreover, waste products of cellular metabolism diffuse into the capillary and are thus carried away in the blood stream.

Throughout the body the course of the veins parallels that of the arteries (Pl. IV). In general, the veins are constructed like their accompanying arteries and arterioles except that their walls are thinner and their caliber, or diameter, is larger. Many veins in the body contain valves (Fig. 10) which prevent the backward flow of venous blood.

Circulatory Dynamics. In order for blood to circulate, it must leave the left ventricle under a certain amount of pressure. How much pressure depends upon the force with which the ventricle contracts and the resistance that the emerging head of blood meets. The chief resistance is the inertia of the blood already in the circulatory vessels throughout the body. The arterioles are the chief regulators of resistance. When their muscular coats contract, resistance to flow is greatly increased. When the smooth muscle of the arterioles relaxes, their caliber widens, blood flows more easily, and the pressure of blood leaving the heart drops.

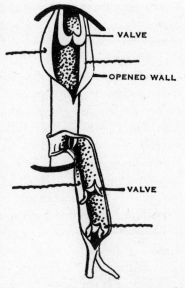

Fig. 10. Vein (partly opened), showing valves.

The arterioles also directly maintain pressure during diastole. If they were completely relaxed, blood entering the arterial system in systole would run off into the tissue capillaries and veins. But the arterioles contract and effectively dam back a fraction of the blood so that it may exert pressure during diastole. If adequate diastolic pressure is to be maintained, the aortic valve must also be able to close tightly. The normal limits of blood pressure are 70 to 90 millimeters of mercury diastolic and 110 to 140 systolic. At these pressures all the organs of the body, including the heart, are adequately supplied with blood from the arteries. As a person gets older, both his systolic and diastolic pressures tend to rise.

It is important to realize that an individual's blood pressure may vary during the day and from day to day. Emotional stimuli can cause the arterioles to constrict by way of the nervous system and by the release of adrenalin and nor-adrenalin (see page 105). With the normal individual these rises of pressure are temporary. The nervous system may also cause the groups of arterioles that supply some organs to constrict more than those that supply others. This mechanism enables the body to shunt blood to the organs that need it most. When an individual loses a great deal of blood during an operation or as a result of some injury, the arterioles of the kidneys and intestines contract and in this way make more blood available for the heart and brain.

Blood that enters the capillaries from the arterioles undergoes a drop in pressure and consequently in velocity. The drop in pressure can be explained on a mechanical basis. If an arteriole is considered to be a tube that terminates in many branches, it is easy to see why the pressure in the many branches is less than in the single tube proper. The branches interconnect and a further drop in pressure results. Because pressure in a capillary and its one-cell-thick walls is reduced, substances such as oxygen can pass from the capillary into the surrounding tissue. Finally, the pressure of the tissues along the course of the capillaries forces into the blood certain waste products of cellular metabolism. The merging capillaries, which now carry unoxygenated blood, unite to form venules. The venules in turn give rise to veins.

Veins that lie in the mass of body muscles are affected by the contraction and relaxation of those muscles. Veins of the leg are squeezed every time the leg muscles contract. They are thus "milked," and the blood within them is forced in the direction of the heart. During relaxation of the leg muscles, blood is prevented from flowing backward by valves that are placed along the course of the veins. In this way venous

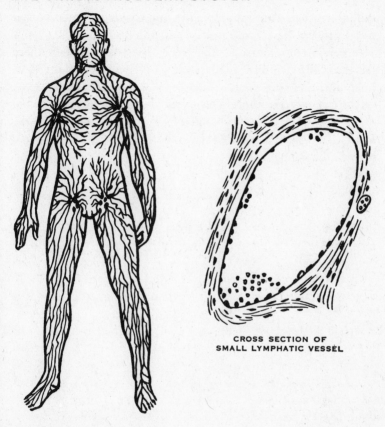

CROSS SECTION OF
SMALL LYMPHATIC VESSEL

Fig. 11. The lymphatic system of the subcutaneous tissue.

blood makes its way to the great venous trunks and then to the heart.

The Lymphatic Vessels. The unique system of lymphatic vessels (Fig. 11) is closely associated with the capillaries in the tissues of the body. These vessels are *not* blood vessels; they carry lymph, a fluid that closely resembles blood plasma. The lymphatics associated with the capillaries are small thin-

23

walled vessels. They join to form increasingly larger vessels which follow the same course as the arteries and veins. Throughout the course of the larger lymphatic vessels there are specialized units of tissue called lymph nodes. Most lymphatics of the body drain into a large central vessel called the thoracic duct. This vessel lies alongside the spinal column and empties into one of the large veins near the heart. The function of the lymph will be fully considered in the following chapter.

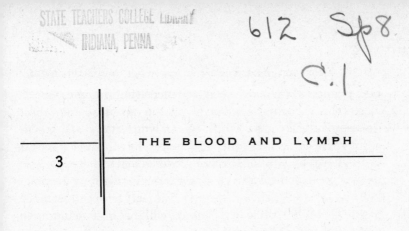

THE BLOOD AND LYMPH

3

BLOOD IS THE MEANS of providing nutrition for billions of cells which engage in an almost endless variety of activities. Even the functions of the highly specialized tissues discussed in the chapter on metabolism (see page 89) depend for their raw materials on the circulating blood.

Some of the blood's substances are in the fluid part called the plasma. Plasma constitutes a little over one half of the blood volume. The remainder is composed of blood cells, which also carry much-needed substances. Some parts of the blood are secretions which are being transported from the the gland where they originate to the cells that require them. Other parts of the blood are waste products now being carried away for elimination.

Various substances are continuously being emptied into and removed from the blood. Yet, in spite of this, the amount of all these substances in the circulating blood at any one time remains surprisingly constant. Except for some variation in children and between the sexes, healthy individuals are enough alike in their blood constituents so that normal levels can be established. The normal levels change in one direction or the other when many organs are not functioning properly. This change can be a simple lead to the seat of trouble. Since bile pigments are eliminated by the liver, the presence of more than the usual amount of bile in the blood may mean disease of the liver or bile tracts. Or products of cell metabolism such as urea or urea nitrogen, which should pass out of the body by way of the urine, will remain at a high level in the blood if the kidneys cannot remove them at a normal rate. No one substance measured can lead to a correct interpretation of the difficulty, but several taken together may give a characteristic pattern of abnormal levels which is sometimes more revealing than examination by any other means. The blood, then, is not only of great importance to our well-being, but it also mirrors many of our illnesses and warns of trouble that cannot be seen.

Fig. 12. Red blood cells.

The cells of the blood fall into two main categories: red cells which give the blood its color, and white cells of several varieties. In addition, fragments of cells called platelets or thrombocytes are a necessary formed element in the blood.

Red cells, called erythrocytes (Fig. 12), are formed in the marrow of the bones, chiefly in the spine and hip bones, the ribs, and the sternum, or breastbone. As they grow, they gradually lose their nucleus before being discharged into the blood and put to work. Their fate is now clear, however. The worker red cell lives only about four months after its nucleus has disappeared. However, replacements are normally continuous, and there is a superabundance of marrow to care for extraordinary needs for red cells.

A red cell in its circulating form is a minute disc which has two concave sides. Ordinarily about thirty-five trillion of these discs are floating through the blood stream at any one time. This number is very easily estimated. Most of us have had a tiny drop of blood drawn from a pricked finger into a measured tube, where it is diluted with a known quantity of solution. After it is shaken well for even distribution this mixture is then spread on an accurately ruled glass slide. Under the microscope the number of red cells

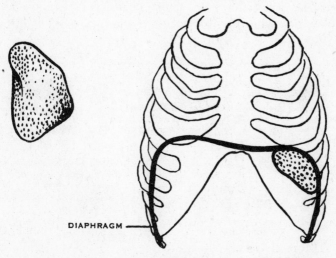

DIAPHRAGM

Fig. 13. The spleen, and its location in the body.

counted on this slide in a square of known size is a clue to the total number available.

How and why the red cells are destroyed in natural processes is not known in all details. The spleen (Fig. 13), however, plays a large role in red-cell destruction. It is a spongelike organ which lies high on the left side of the abdomen near the stomach and diaphragm. The blood, instead of coursing through channels in the spleen, is slowed in its passage by the intricacies of the spongy structure. Here it is that the red cells' final disintegration takes place.

The erythrocytes (red cells) are red because of their content of hemoglobin, a protein combined with an iron-containing pigment. This compound is of greatest importance because it makes possible the transportation from lung to body cell of the oxygen necessary for life. It does so in a very simple manner. When a breath of good air has been drawn in, oxygen of high concentration surrounds the blood in the lung. The iron of the hemoglobin then rapidly forms a loose combination with this oxygen and the red cell is off to distant

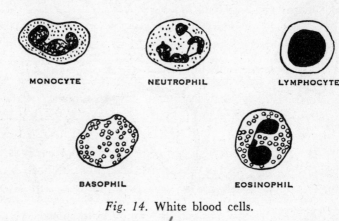

MONOCYTE   NEUTROPHIL   LYMPHOCYTE

BASOPHIL   EOSINOPHIL

Fig. 14. White blood cells.

parts. In the organs that have been using oxygen, hemoglobin now finds itself surrounded by low oxygen tension. It promptly gives up much of its loosely bound load. On the return journey from organs to lung through the veins, another gas replaces the oxygen. This is carbon dioxide, which is being released from the active tissue cells. It is carried away by the blood and given off into the air of the lung for discharge from the body. While much of the carbon dioxide joins hemoglobin, it also occurs in the blood plasma as bicarbonate of sodium.

It is common knowledge that human beings cannot tolerate the presence in the atmosphere of a gas that will be preferred by hemoglobin. Carbon monoxide is rapidly lethal. It combines with hemoglobin more readily than does oxygen, and this replacement can cause death in a few hours if it is not reversed.

Iron is an essential part of hemoglobin and hence of the red cell. When iron is deficient in the diet, fewer red cells are formed, and/or their pigment content is less. This is one kind of anemia that physicians easily remedy by giving iron or by feeding foods with a high iron content.

For a variety of reasons many individuals do not have enough red blood cells. They may have lost blood through hemorrhage. Chronic infections can depress the bone marrow or destroy erythrocytes. The cells may be formed in insufficient quantity because of lack of a substance called erythrocyte-maturing factor, which is formed in the stomach and stored in the liver. The taking of liver or liver extract allows the return of normal red-cell formation. Anemia is a common disability which accompanies many illnesses, but fortunately red-cell restoration is usually possible and often spontaneous on recovery.

The white blood cells, called leucocytes, are of several kinds (Fig. 14). The polymorphonuclear cells, or "polys," as they are often called, are recognized because they have granules which stain in particular ways in laboratory tests. The most abundant of these are the neutrophils, so called because they are neutral to acid or basic dyes. The neutrophils are the cells that are strongly attracted to certain bacteria or to dead tissue within the body. By liberating substances which help to digest and liquefy the infected or dead tissue they aid in its removal. The neutrophils are also phagocytes—that is, they ingest or absorb bacteria in an engulfing process called

Fig. 15. Phagocytosis of bacteria by neutrophils.

phagocytosis (Fig. 15). In this process the entire bacterium particle is taken into the interior of the cell, where it is then digested. At times, however, the bacteria win and remain alive even within the cell.

The eosinophilic "polys," which show bright red granules when stained with acid dyes, are ordinarily present in much smaller numbers than the neutrophils. Their function is not clear, but they tend to become more numerous in the blood in allergic states or when parasites such as worms are present in the body.

The leucocytes called basophilic, because their granules stain with basic dyes, do not serve a useful purpose as far as is known. They may, however, be related to the basophiles that are found in certain tissues called mast cells. The basophilic granules of the mast cells contain heparin, which acts against some of the clotting factors in the blood.

All these polymorphonuclear leucocytes (white cells) are formed in good part in the bone marrow along with the red cells. How long they live and where they die has not been traced. Probably many are destroyed at the particular site where their work is being carried out.

After the "polys," the lymphocytes are the most abundant of the leucocytes in the circulating blood. They are also very numerous within most organs of the body, especially in the structures called lymph nodes through which lymph flows on its way from the tissues to the blood. The lymphocytes seem to be related in some way to the formation of antibodies, the mechanisms by which the body becomes immune to disease or infection. Then the lymph nodes are especially active and become enlarged in the neighborhood of an area of infection or where some dead tissue is being removed. We are all familiar with the tender swollen "glands" that may appear in the neck when we have a sore throat. In reality these are swollen lymph nodes.

The monocytes complete the list of the leucocytes of the blood. The monocytes have little or no known activity in the circulating blood, but they are close relatives of the macrophages which are developed in lymph nodes, spleen, and lymphoid areas in the organs. The macrophages are phagocytes and are the chief scavengers of the body. While the "polys" ingest bacteria, the macrophages engulf particles of tissue from areas destroyed by disease. They are more actively engaged than any other cells in engulfing, or phagocytosis, for the removal of foreign particles. These particular phagocytes, the macrophages, do not circulate in the blood.

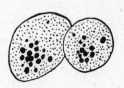

Fig. 16.
Blood platelets.

When doctors check our physical state, one of their most common procedures is to count the number of leucocytes in a drop of blood from the finger and to determine the percentage of each kind of leucocyte in a smear of a drop of blood on a glass slide. Some illnesses are reflected in a change in the level of circulating leucocytes of one type or another. Many infections are accompanied by a rise in the leucocyte count, or leucocytosis. This is an indication that one defense mechanism against infection is in proper order.

A third formed element found in the blood is called a platelet or thrombocyte (Fig. 16). Platelets are not actually cells. They are derived from fragments of giant cells, the megakaryocytes, found in the bone marrow, and as they circulate in the blood they are the smallest form that can be counted in the microscope. They have a somewhat sticky quality and tend to adhere to a roughened surface such as an injured blood vessel. Here they clump together, disintegrate, and liberate thrombokinase, a substance which starts the process of blood clotting.

Very many different substances are necessary for the clotting of the blood. Only the most important ones will be mentioned here. These substances react together to form thrombin, which is an enzyme. Thrombin acts, in turn, on fibrinogen, a protein which is formed mostly by the liver cells. Thrombin acting on fibrinogen converts the latter into the clot, called fibrin.

The relationship of the most important substances in blood clotting can be indicated in these two steps:

Thrombokinase + prothrombin + calcium + several accessory factors = thrombin

Thrombin + fibrinogen = fibrin (the clot)

Thrombokinase occurs either in platelets or in the blood plasma, where it is activated by platelets. Prothrombin is formed by the liver when enough vitamin K has been absorbed from the intestinal tract. Calcium is in the circulating blood in small quantities usually sufficient for its required role in the clotting mechanism. Many of the accessory factors are still being studied; their mode of action is not clear.

But why doesn't the blood clot all the time if all these substances are present? There are many reasons. For thrombokinase to be released, the platelets must disintegrate, as they will if blood flows over a rough surface. Besides this, there is in the blood an antithrombin which counteracts the action of thrombin. A third factor is this: when a fibrin clot forms, thrombin tends to be adsorbed to its threads and is thus removed from further action.

The fluid nature of the blood as it flows through the vascular system, then, depends upon a balance of the factors for and against coagulation, or clotting. Clots do form especially in the veins of the legs, where pressure is lower. They may originate near an infected area or from pressure on the vein. Some clots develop in relation to an operation. However they can be counteracted by the giving of anticoagulant drugs.

The blood cells are suspended in a fluid plasma which appears light yellow and watery when it is separated from the cells. In solution it contains very many substances, the details of which would be tedious. The important components of plasma can be grouped as follows:

A. Organic constituents
   1. Proteins
      a. Albumin, which is largely responsible for maintaining the blood by attracting water into the blood vessels.
      b. Globulins, proteins important for their role in immunity to disease.
      c. Fibrinogen, which is the precursor of fibrin, the meshwork of the blood clot.
   2. Carbohydrates such as glucose and other simple sugars for energy production.
   3. Fats and related substances, lipids, such as cholesterol and phospholipids for utilization or storage.
   4. Products of cell activity or metabolism, such as amino acids, urea, and uric acid, many of which are to be eliminated.

5. Internal secretions, antibodies, and enzymes of varied chemical constitution, passing from the tissues where they originate to those which will utilize them.

B. Inorganic constituents

Important ones are sodium, chloride, calcium, phosphorus, potassium, carbonates, present in various combinations.

Blood Groups. During World War I we first became generally aware of the importance of blood transfusions. Sudden loss of large quantities of blood may be fatal. But a transfusion of blood from an individual who can well afford to donate a pint or two may save the life of an ill or wounded person until his own bone marrow can replace the red cells.

Our use of blood transfusions has become steadily more frequent both in wartime and in civilian life. However, great caution must be exercised to insure that blood be given from a donor belonging to a compatible blood group. Before World War I, Landsteiner and others had worked out the major blood groups to some one of which we each belong. While today much more is known of other factors involved, Landsteiner's original groups are still regarded as the important ones. To decide whether the donor's blood "matches" the recipient's blood a test can be performed to see whether the serum (that is, plasma without fibrinogen) can be added to the red cells of the recipient without causing clumping or agglutination of the cells. If the red cells throughout the body were to agglutinate, many would disintegrate; other clumps would plug small capillaries; and the recipient would be seriously ill.

There are four main groups of blood classified according to whether the red cells or the serum have one or another agglutinating factor, or have neither, or have both. These groups are as follows:

Group A: Has A agglutinating factor in his red cells, and Anti-B in his serum.

Group B: Has B agglutinating factor in his red cells, and Anti-A in his serum.

Group AB: Has both A and B agglutinating factor in his red cells, but none of the factors in his serum.

Group O: Has none of the factors in his red cells, but Anti-A and B in his serum.

An individual whose blood falls into Group A or B or AB can give or receive blood from his corresponding group. In an emergency, Group O blood can be used for anyone, since its red cells are free of any factors and the serum factor is less important. For this reason a man with Group O blood is called a universal donor. This is the most common group in our population.

One other agglutinating factor is commonly tested before blood is regarded as properly matched. This is the Rh factor, so named for the first two letters of rhesus, the species of monkey in which it was first found. About 85 per cent of us have this factor in our blood and are said to be Rh positive. The remaining 15 per cent of Rh-negative individuals might chance to receive Rh-positive blood if they required a transfusion. They would then become "sensitized" to it and another transfusion of Rh-positive blood could bring about serious destruction of red cells.

Other factors causing agglutination on transfusion of blood are rare compared with the above and tests are not commonly made for them.

Exchange of Fluid. All the tissues of the body are moist. The cells themselves contain fluid and are bathed by free tissue fluid. There is a constant circulation of fluid between the blood and the body tissues which facilitates the exchange of dissolved substances. There are two main forces which govern the interchange of fluid between the blood and the tissue. One, the hydrostatic pressure of the blood, or the force tending to drive fluid out through the capillary wall into the tissue, is dependent upon the force of the heartbeat, the blood volume, the weight of the column of blood when the body is erect, and other factors.

Counterbalancing the force of the hydrostatic pressure is the osmotic pressure, which tends to attract water from the tissues back into the blood. The osmotic pressure is dependent upon the presence of molecules in solution in the blood. Nonprotein constituents such as salt, sugar, and urea, can pass freely through the capillary wall to the tissues; hence their concentration will be the same in blood and tissue fluids. But protein does not easily penetrate the capillary wall, and only a small amount enters the tissue spaces. Therefore, at some point the protein of the blood is greater and tends to attract fluid from the tissue back into the circulation. Or, in other words, the osmotic pressure of the blood is greater than that of the tissue fluid.

The manner in which these two pressures, hydrostatic and osmotic, act can now be seen. As the blood enters the capillary its hydrostatic force is greatest and a dilute plasma with little protein tends to pass out into the tissues. As the blood continues along the capillary, its hydrostatic pressure drops, but the blood is now more concentrated. Or, specifically, its protein content is higher so that fluid tends to return to it near the venous end of the capillary. The returning fluid contains salts but no protein. The latter does not return to the blood through the capillary, but does eventually get there by the lymph.

The lymph channels resemble capillaries in structure, but are much more permeable than the blood capillaries. Their walls offer practically no barrier to proteins and they are therefore the special channel whereby protein is returned to the blood.

The lymph can even pick up matter composed of separate particles. At frequent intervals the lymph channels enter and emerge from lymph nodes, the special collections of lymphoid tissue which are often referred to as "glands." Here, in addition to lymphocytes and cells with an antibody content, there are many phagocytes to engulf particles and thus fight infection.

The lymph nodes near the lung are black, because the lymph from the lung carries out the coal dust we breathe. When a finger is infected, the lymph nodes in the armpit may become swollen and tender as the lymph drains bacteria into this spot. Lymph nodes are protective in many ways.

The flow of lymph along the lymph channels is less forcefully directed than is the blood, since lymph does not have the propulsion force of the heartbeat. Lymph is aided in its movement by muscle contraction, respiratory movements, and increase in fluid in particular parts. If the flow of lymph is impeded, it can reverse its direction and follow another pathway through connections with other lymphatics. Eventually the intricate network of lymphatics joins larger trunks, still with very delicate walls, until the main lymph vessels empty into two large veins not far from the right side of the heart.

The relationship of lymph, tissue fluid surrounding cells, intracellular fluid, and the blood plasma is further discussed in the section dealing with water metabolism (see page 95).

LIKE THE BEATING of the heart and the circulation of the blood, breathing is of vital importance for the immediate preservation of life. As we shall see in the chapter explaining metabolism (see page 89), a continuous supply of oxygen is necessary for the essential functioning of each cell in the body. The oxygen supply comes from air drawn into the lungs. It permeates the body by way of the blood in the arteries and is exchanged for a waste gas, carbon dioxide. This gas returns in the venous blood to the lungs and is expelled. Interruption of this cycle for only a few minutes by suffocation or strangulation causes death because the respiratory center in the brain will not start the breathing process again. However, if the time elapsed is not too great, artificial production of breathing may lead to resumption of the natural movements, and life continues.

Normally the breath drawn in consists of air with its oxygen, nitrogen, carbon dioxide, and water vapor along with all the fumes and solid particles it is our misfortune to dwell among. But the breathing process may also be used to administer drugs in gas form. This was the first method developed for production of general anesthesia and it is still in common use today. Only a trained individual can safely

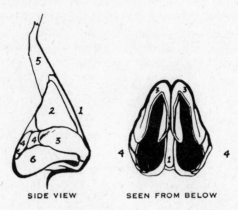

SIDE VIEW   SEEN FROM BELOW

Fig. 17. The external nose. 1. Cartilage of septum. 2. Lateral cartilage. 3. Greater alar. 4. Lesser alar. 5. Nasal bone. 6. Fibrofatty tissue.

introduce a foreign gas into the lungs and still maintain proper oxygenation of the cells, however.

The respiratory system can readily be thought of in two main divisions. The first or upper part conducts air and, as a corollary of this action, produces the voice. It consists of the nose, pharynx, larynx, trachea, and bronchial tree, and forms continuous passageways from the face through the neck and midportion of the chest to the terminal small bronchi deep in the lungs (Pl. VI and Pl. VII). The second part of the respiratory system receives the air and exchanges gases. This action occurs throughout the spongy structure of the lungs, which occupy the major part of the cavity on both sides of the chest.

Air is necessary for life, but in most human habitations it contains injurious material. If it were not for the protective action of the respiratory passages, the lungs would be continually subjected to damage that would shorten our lives. The nose (Fig. 17) has two portals of entry separated by a flexible dividing wall. Its delicate lining is constantly active in removing impurities from the air we take in. The hairs visible at the nostrils strain out larger particles. A sticky but fluid mucus is secreted all along the inner passage to catch and wash out more dirt. The city dweller is all too often made aware of the contamination of the air by the blackness of his nostrils.

Besides the hairs at the nose's portals and the mucus of its lining, a third protective mechanism is the constant beating of microscopic hairlike projections called cilia, which extend from the surface of the lining cells. The cilia are extraordinarily proficient in propelling dust toward the outside. Unfortunately many people with nasal infection thoughtlessly apply substances to the passages of the nose which lessen the activity of the cilia and only aid the spread of the infection.

The mucous membrane of the nose contains an exceptional number of capillaries. They diffuse a flow of warm blood which effectively reduces the chill of the air we breathe. On the debit side of the ledger is the fact that these many capillaries rapidly become congested when we have a cold. Then the swollen lining alone may obstruct the passageway of the nose. Nasal sprays and applications are designed to cause contraction of these capillaries and so reduce their swelling.

Communicating with the nasal cavity are pockets in the facial bones, called sinuses (Pl. VI and Fig. 18), which are lined by ciliated mucous membrane similar to that in the nose. The sinuses contribute to the fluid secretion for the protective washing-out process, as we are aware when infection of a sinus increases this discharge.

From the nose the respiratory passages turn a right angle downward to become the pharynx, which forms the throat that is visible through the open mouth. Since the pharynx plays the dual role of allowing food as well as air to enter

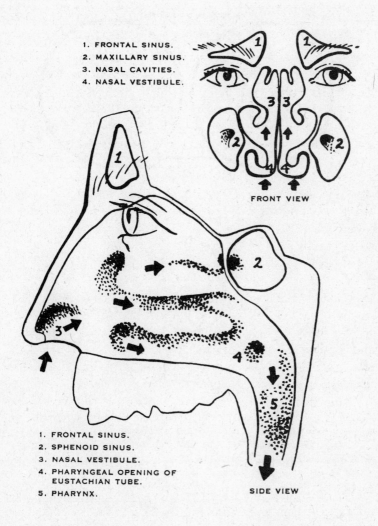

1. FRONTAL SINUS.
2. MAXILLARY SINUS.
3. NASAL CAVITIES.
4. NASAL VESTIBULE.

FRONT VIEW

1. FRONTAL SINUS.
2. SPHENOID SINUS.
3. NASAL VESTIBULE.
4. PHARYNGEAL OPENING OF
   EUSTACHIAN TUBE.
5. PHARYNX.

SIDE VIEW

Fig. 18. Nasal cavities and sinuses. Arrows show the direction of inhaled air.

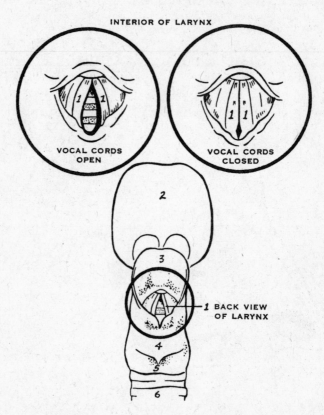

Fig. 19. Diagram of the larynx, showing the epiglottis and vocal cords. 1. Vocal cords. 2. Tongue. 3. Epiglottis. 4. Arytenoid cartilage. 5. Cricoid cartilage. 6. Trachea.

below, it is lined by a tougher membrane more comparable to the skin than is the lining of the nose. Delicate cilia could never survive the rough contact with swallowed food.

In its downward extension the pharynx divides into the larynx for taking in air and the esophagus for taking in food

Fig. 20. The trachea (front view), showing branching into the bronchi. (Arrow indicates the direction of in-haled air.) 1. Epiglottis. 2. Thyroid cartilage. 3. Cricoid cartilage. 4. Trachea. 5. Primary bronchi.

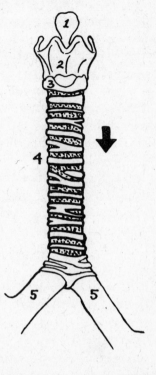

(Pl. VII and Pl. X). The entrance of the larynx (Fig. 19) is protected by a flap of cartilage, called the epiglottis. During the act of swallowing the larynx rises and contracts to prevent the entrance of food or drink into the lungs.

The larynx, from which the sound of the voice originates, has a vulnerable location in the front of the neck; but it is protected by a plate of armor, the thyroid cartilage, popularly known as the "Adam's apple." It is more prominent and sharp in males, and its configuration determines to some extent the deepness of the voice.

Within the larynx the vocal cords stretch across the cavity in the form of a V, with the apex toward the front. They are sharp folds of tissue attached to the sides of the larynx by membranes. Sounds of different intensity and pitch are produced by changes in the vibration and tautness of the vocal cords as air is forcefully expelled over them. The chambers of the mouth and nose account for some of the quality of the sound, and the movement of the lips and tongue are largely responsible for the fashioning of words.

The trachea (Fig. 20) is an uncomplicated straight tube leading from the larynx to the bronchi. Its upper portion is still in the neck, covered only by the soft thyroid gland and by muscles. Despite the fact that the trachea's wall contains firm rings of cartilage, it can be compressed in the act of strangulation.

We are glad, however, that the trachea is so exposed when it becomes necessary to make an emergency opening for someone whose airway is closed above. A baby's larynx is so tiny it can readily close when it is infected. Many a child owes his life to the procedure of opening the trachea.

The trachea enters the chest cavity and divides into two main branches, the bronchi, one leading to either lung. This two-way branching occurs at the level of the second rib under the breastbone, or sternum. The relationships of the trachea at its branching point are important. The main artery of the body, the aorta, curves over it. The esophagus, part of the food passage, lies immediately behind it. Large lymph nodes draining the lung encircle it. Enlargement of any of these structures due to disease may encroach on the others at this spot.

The trachea is also lined by ciliated mucous membrane. The function of these lining structures is mainly a house-cleaning one: the waving cilia hand the fine dirt and secretions along like a bucket brigade; and the mucous glands provide a cohesive material to hold the foreign matter from the lungs. But the lining structures have a far greater importance than mere cleanliness and comfort. They are essential to prevent the entrance of bacteria into the lungs. These bacteria which are so numerous and harmless in the mouth or in the upper respiratory passages can cause serious injury to the lungs and should not pass the first line of defense, the nasal passages and trachea. Sometimes longstanding or repeated infections change the lining of the nasal passages and trachea in such a way that the cilia are destroyed and the mucous membrane becomes dry like the skin. Then the entrance of injurious bacteria is quite likely to occur.

Of greatest importance is the continued functioning of the cough reflex. We are occasionally impressed with the need for a strong cough mechanism to remove from the larynx or trachea a bulky mass such as food or a child's little toy. This need, however, is very rare as compared with the constant duty to cough up even small amounts of liquid which may be carrying bacteria from the mouth or which may in themselves be destructive to the delicate lung tissues. Doctors and nurses know this and are careful not to allow any liquids to be swallowed when the throat has been painted with an anesthetic or when a person is not fully conscious. By dropping into the mouth of a sleeping person a little of the radio-opaque oil which forms a shadow in an x-ray, one can easily demonstrate what happens to an oily substance when there is no cough. The next morning an x-ray picture will show the oil deep in the lower parts of the lungs. It can run down unhampered in a sleeping individual whose cough reflex is very inactive.

The bronchi (Pl. VII and Fig. 21) lead into the lungs and branch to make a treelike formation within them. The larger bronchi have cartilaginous rings just as the trachea does. The smaller branches are tubes of muscle, elastic, and collagen fibers capable of expanding and extending. They vary in diameter with the expansion and release of the lungs during breathing. The small bronchi at the ends are of special interest. They are encircled by a muscle coat heavier than elsewhere and capable of markedly narrowing the passages. Narrowing occurs when someone with asthma has an attack. His allergic reaction is in the form of spasm of these muscles. We can hear the obstruction as a noisy, prolonged period of expulsion of air past the narrowed small bronchi.

The small muscular bronchi are also active in passing on

upward dust and germs and excessive mucus in final protection of the vulnerable lung tissues. In addition to the action of cilia and mucus there is a wavelike contraction, or peristalsis, of these bronchi similar to that of the intestine, which pushes bulky material in the direction of the wave. This peristalsis is a substitute for the sudden effect of a cough, since a stimulus deep in the lungs does not provoke the cough reflex.

The importance of the peristaltic waves is indicated when a severe infection of these muscular bronchi results in destruction of the muscle necessary for contraction. It is not sufficient that the bronchi are open tubes allowing the passage of air into and from the lungs. They must be active participants in the war against injurious agents attempting to enter the air sacs of the lung. That is why a portion of the

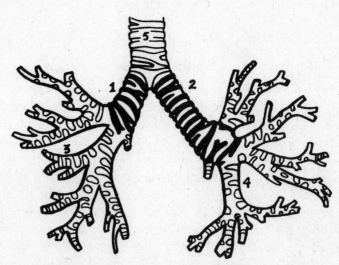

Fig. 21. The lower trachea and bronchi. 1. Right primary bronchus. 2. Left primary bronchus. 3. Right secondary bronchi. 4. Left secondary bronchi. 5. Trachea.

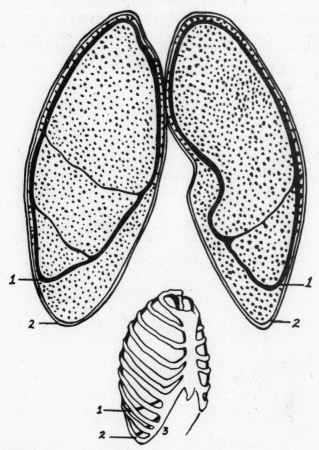

Fig. 22. The thorax, lungs, and pleura. 1. Lower margin of the lungs. 2. Lower margin of the pleura. 3. Lower rib margin.

lung is often removed surgically when the bronchi can no longer move well enough to evacuate themselves.

The Lungs. The lungs are voluminous organs almost as large as, but much lighter than, the liver (Pl. VIII). Each completely fills its side of the chest cavity and lies close to the pericardial sac which surrounds the heart. The lungs are covered by a delicate membrane, the pleura (Fig. 22), which is folded back over the inner side of the chest wall. Only a potential space exists between these two layers of the pleura, but fluid can collect there due to heart failure or inflammation of the pleura, called pleurisy. Then this fluid may require removal for easier breathing.

The lungs of a newborn baby are pink, but most adults have taken in enough dust so that their lungs are colored

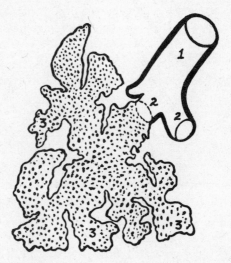

Fig. 23. Lung alveoli. 1. Bronchiole (small bronchus). 2. Alveolar ducts. 3. Alveoli.

gray with black streaks. Lungs resemble a sponge only superficially. They can be squeezed much as a sponge is squeezed, and they have many air-filled pockets, but the structure of the lung is more orderly than that of a sponge. All the many fine branches of the bronchial tree lead into scalloped sacs, called alveoli (Fig. 23). An alveolus is the ultimate unit of the respiratory system and is the spot where gas interchanges between air and blood. The walls of the alveoli are admirably suited to this purpose. They are very delicate, hardly more than a network of capillaries intermingled with a few strands of elastic and collagen fibers. These fibers, however, are sufficient to give a healthy lung the elastic recoil it needs to expel air from its sacs.

The manner in which the air spaces and their bronchi are fitted together reminds one of a large apartment house. The alveoli, or rooms, open only into the private hall, the individual fine bronchus, which in turn communicates with the main hallways. The rooms of adjacent apartments are close to each other, but there are no doors leading from one apartment to another. However, the walls of the air sacs are delicate and somewhat porous so that individual cells and fluid can pass through the wall from one sac into another. The passing may continue until it encounters heavier walls which really form barriers to further spreading of cells and fluid through the lungs. These barriers are fibrous dividing walls which surround small subdivisions of the lung. They can help to keep some unwanted material, especially infective organisms, in one part of the lung; and thus, by localizing the action, they can at least reduce the damage these organisms do.

The largest division of the lung tissue is the lobe, of which there are two on the left, and three on the right. These lobes do not communicate with each other except as their bronchi emerge from a common stem. Disease of one lobe of the lung is very likely to remain localized to that lobe. That is why a surgeon can often effect a cure by removing that lobe before the disease spreads by the bronchial or blood channels.

Now that the structure of the respiratory system has been

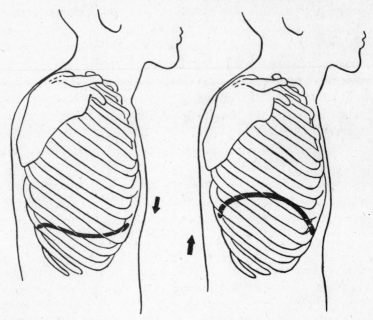

Fig. 24. Diagram of a person inhaling. Arrow indicates the direction in which the diaphragm moves.

Fig. 25. Diagram of a person exhaling. Arrow indicates the direction in which the diaphragm moves.

described, the mechanism of breathing remains to be explained. The active force bringing about inhalation, or the entrance of air, is not the lung itself, but the chest muscles and the diaphragm. As the chest muscles contract they draw the ribs up and outward. At the same time the diaphragm—the muscle wall which separates the chest cavity from the abdominal cavity—contracts. At rest it is in the form of a rounded tent. When it contracts, it flattens down and so enlarges the chest cavity (Fig. 24). The lungs immediately expand to fill the cavity, since a vacuum cannot exist between the chest wall and the lung. The tension of the gas in the lung is lowered by this expansion and the atmospheric air of higher pressure rushes in. This is inhalation.

Exhalation is largely a passive occurrence. The chest muscles and diaphragm relax (Fig. 25), the ribs drop back closer together, the lungs recoil, and air is expelled quietly.

Before a newborn infant draws in his first breath, his chest capacity is small and the air sacs in his lungs are collapsed. When the first contraction of the respiratory muscles, described above, enlarges the chest, the lungs must also expand to a point where they fill the entire space. This they can do because of the arrangement of elastic and collagen fibers in the walls of the alveoli and bronchi. A vigorous cry aids in this first expansion of the infant's lungs and is essential to keep out the infection which tends to settle in inactive, nonemptying parts of the lungs.

After the baby breathes out, his lungs never return to their collapsed state, but remain partly open with some residual air. And they are always under tension as they are held open by the chest wall.

In quiet breathing a person inhales a certain amount of air which mixes with the residual air, and a similar amount is exhaled. This is called tidal air and represents only a part of the breathing capacity of the individual. If he continues to inhale beyond his usual breath to the point of the greatest expansion he can achieve, an additional amount of air, called complemental air, will be taken in. Also, after a quiet expiration he can force more air out of his lungs. This is called supplemental air. All of these—the ordinary tidal air, the complemental inhalation, and the supplemental exhalation —are included when the vital capacity of the lungs is measured.

A healthy young person has good elastic recoil of the lungs and his vital capacity is high. In an older individual the spine is curved and the rib cage increased in contour so that the chest is larger, and the elastic recoil of the lung tissues is diminished. The lungs remain in a greater state of expansion, the residual air is greater, and vital capacity is reduced.

The ultimate function of the lung is to provide oxygen to the blood as it circulates through the lung capillaries, and to remove from it excess carbon dioxide for discharge into the air. This two-way exchange is not governed by the activity of any cells. It occurs because of the differences between the partial pressure of the various gases in the air sacs and that of the blood in the sac walls. When air has just been breathed in there is a higher pressure of oxygen in this air than in the pulmonary capillary blood, because that blood has just returned from organs which have utilized its oxygen. Accordingly oxygen will diffuse in the direction of lower pressure—into the blood. Carbon dioxide, on the other hand, has a greater partial pressure in the blood of the lungs than in the fresh air and will diffuse toward the lower pressure, or out of the blood into the air of the alveoli (air sacs). Any abnormal gas that may be present in the air breathed in is sure to be taken into the blood promptly, since its pressure there would be zero. We all know how rapidly a gas used for anesthesia enters the blood, travels to the brain, and is effective in bringing about unconsciousness.

Other less obvious functions of respiration deal with the fact that water vapor is present in a higher concentration in air breathed out than in air inhaled. When water is given off by evaporation the tissues are cooled, as any object would be. While the lungs are not as important a means of evaporation as the skin, they do contribute and their action can be increased when the need is greater. The panting dog on a hot day is relieving himself by losing more water with each exhalation. Panting is less effective on a humid day, since the air taken into the lungs is more saturated with moisture, and less water is removed from the body.

Because we lose moisture in exhaling, it follows naturally that respiration contributes to the regulation of the amount of water in the body. Hot weather brings with it a greater thirst because of the greater evaporation from the body surfaces and the lungs.

The action of the lungs also plays a part in the regulation of acidity, or pH, in the blood. Other things being equal, the more carbon dioxide there is present in fluid the more acid the fluid becomes. While we have many means of combating the effect of excessive carbon dioxide in order to maintain a normal acid level, continued excess may contribute to the development of acidosis. Fortunately carbon dioxide is itself a stimulus to the respiratory center of the brain, and tends to bring about more rapid breathing and greater expulsion of the carbon dioxide.

5

THIS LONG CHANNEL (Pl. X) which occupies a major part of the body is commonly called the digestive system. Digestion is, of course, a necessary step for providing nutrition to the organs, but absorption into the blood and lymph stream of material digested is equally necessary and equally interesting. The alimentary tract is also the means of eliminating from the body nonabsorbable components of food, masses of bacteria, and the products of cell activities.

While the tissues throughout the body depend in good part on the continued taking in of food so that they can obtain materials for their specific functions and so that they can replace themselves, there is not the same immediacy about eating as there is about breathing. Death from lack of oxygen occurs in a matter of minutes. We can, however, exist for several weeks without taking in any food. This large margin of safety depends upon storage of the products of digestion in many organs so that these products may be utilized when outside replenishment is not available. The alimentary system's peak of activity, then, is periodic according to our eating habits, which are dictated more by custom than by the rigid demands of the body.

The alimentary tract is readily divided into many parts,

all continuous but quite individual in structure and behavior.

The Mouth. The first section, the mouth (Pl. XI), is far more than just a cavity for the reception of food and drink. An important but not absolutely essential part of digestion occurs in the mouth, and requires the vigorous action of the teeth and tongue, and especially of the digestive juices supplied by the salivary glands (Pl. X and Pl. XII). Two of the latter, the parotid glands, lie in front of the lower extremity of the ear, at the angle of the jaw. These are the glands which become swollen and tender with the "mumps." The two sublingual glands lie beneath the tongue near the front, and the submaxillary glands are located beneath the lower jaw toward the midline. These organs are composed almost entirely of cells of secretion, capable of discharging varying quantities of digestive solution into the mouth through ducts. They secrete small amounts constantly, but are induced to pour out larger quantities by such stimuli as the sight or smell of attractive food. This is a reflex, not a thoughtful reaction. Salivation is also increased by the mechanical stimulus of something in the mouth, such as chewing gum or even the finger.

Over 99 per cent of saliva is water. The remainder is composed of inorganic salts and of organic material, including the starch-splitting enzyme ptyalin. As solid food is crushed by the powerful tongue and the grinding action of the teeth, saliva is thoroughly mixed with small food particles, and the digestion of starch to simpler sugar is carried out by the ptyalin. It continues, however, in the stomach if the acid gastric juice does not stop the action of the ptyalin.

The salts are active ingredients of saliva. One of them, bicarbonate, helps to maintain a constant alkalinity of the salivary juices. (It is in an optimum degree of acidity or alkalinity that each enzyme acts.) Other salts, calcium phos-

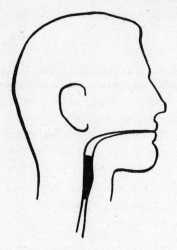

Fig. 26. The pharynx, indicated by dark area.

phate and calcium carbonate, are sometimes deposited on the teeth with organic material, but not in useful form. We remove this tartar, as it is called, by brushing and scraping to keep the teeth clean.

When the food is reduced in size and moistened enough to slip back to the throat, the act of swallowing starts. Only the beginning of this process is voluntary. Once the pharynx (Fig. 26), that common passage for food and air, is reached, the soft uvula, which hangs from the palate, rises to close the nasal passages (Pl. XI, Mouth). Contraction of muscles around the larynx raises and constricts the vocal-cord region, effectively preventing entrance of food into the lungs. The powerful force of the tongue's thrust and the contraction of the muscles of the pharynx shoot food or liquid into the next major section.

The Esophagus. The esophagus (Fig. 27) is a slightly curved hollow tube, about ten inches long, extending from the midneck region to the stomach in the upper abdomen. It courses down the midportion of the chest behind the heart, close to the main artery, the aorta. For a time it lies alongside the trachea, which branches in front of it. Enlargement of the heart can press on the esophagus and create some degree of obstruction and distress.

The esophagus is lined by the same relatively tough, multilayered membrane that is found in the mouth. This membrane can tolerate rough objects which would injure the delicate ciliated lining of the respiratory passages. The wall of the esophagus is encircled by layers of muscle and fibrous tissue. Their vigorous contractions in a series of waves force the softened food ahead into the stomach regardless of the position the body adopts. We are not often called upon to swallow solids while standing on our heads, but food would be forced ahead of the contractions even under such circum-

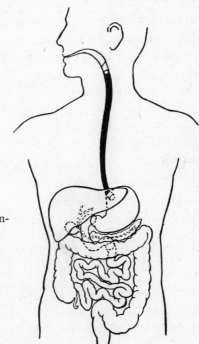

Fig. 27. The esophagus, indicated by dark area.

stances. We are aware, of course, that being flat in bed does not interfere at all with the swallowing process and the progress of the food.

Fluids do not require the action of the peristaltic wave described above. The thrust of the tongue shoots them forcibly down the esophagus and into the stomach. Chewed or masticated food and liquids do not undergo any further digestive change during their passage through the esophagus. It is only a connecting tunnel from the throat to the abdominal alimentary organs (Pl. X).

The esophagus, after passing through the diaphragm which separates the chest from the abdomen, immediately opens into the stomach. This opening is called the cardiac end of the stomach, or the cardia, a name which indicates its nearness to the heart. When a little acid juice from the stomach is regurgitated into the esophagus with belching, an individual may say he has "heartburn" because he associates this location with his heart.

The Stomach. The stomach (Pl. X and Fig. 28) is a distensible sac lying mainly in the left upper portion of the abdomen. It is in somewhat the form of a J, the hook extending across the abdomen's midline to lie close to the undersurface of the liver. Its contour reminds one of a closed hammock slung between esophagus and duodenum. The greater part of its thick wall is formed of coats of muscle capable of strong contractions in the form of peristaltic waves.

The mucous lining of the stomach is unique in structure and forms specific secretions for the digestion of food. This lining is thrown into folds, the pattern of which can be detected in an x-ray picture if material opaque to the x-ray is swallowed. In the stomach many of the digestive processes are begun as the food remains from one to two hours in the sac closed at either end by contracted muscle.

The entrance of food into the stomach stimulates the out-pouring of more secretions, and the contractions of the wall become more active. As the food becomes increasingly soft-ened and disintegrated, it is acted upon by gastric enzymes,

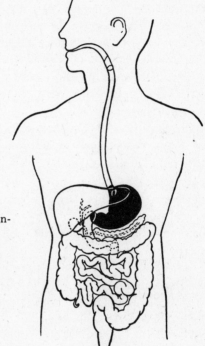

Fig. 28. The stomach, in-dicated by dark area.

of which pepsin, a protein-splitting one, is the most essential. Pepsin is secreted by glands lining the upper half of the stomach. It acts best when the gastric juice is acid. This en-zyme, pepsin, starts the changing of proteins to less complex substances by separating their component parts, known as proteoses and peptones. This is not the final stage of disin-tegration, but is as far as it is carried in the stomach.

Rennin is a milk-curdling enzyme especially abundant in

the young. It too is formed in good part by the upper half of the stomach's mucous membrane. The protein of the precipitated milk curd is then acted upon by pepsin as above.

There is also an enzyme, a lipase, which splits fat, but its action is insignificant compared with the digestion of fat in the intestine.

Starch continues to be broken down by the swallowed saliva until the gastric juice becomes too acid for ptyalin to act.

The glands within the mucous membrane of the stomach (Pl. XII) contain a variety of cells, some of which secrete mucin, others hydrochloric acid, and others the digestive enzymes mentioned. The acid-forming cells in the lower half of the stomach actually secrete a very strong acid which would be injurious to the lining of the stomach if it were not partly neutralized by the basic mucin. When the balance between mucin and acid is disturbed so that the contents of the stomach cavity are too acid, irritations such as gastritis or destruction of parts of the wall, known as ulcers, are likely to result.

As might be expected, secretions are not poured out in constant amounts, but vary in quantity in relation to the taking of food. This means that in the period two to three hours after a meal there is less mucus secretion to neutralize the effect of the acid. A healthy stomach is not aware of this increased acidity. Someone with an inflamed gastric mucous membrane or with an ulcer, however, feels pain or burning discomfort, which is relieved by a simple neutralizer such as milk.

Hydrochloric acid is not to be regarded only as an irritant which must be combated, however. It serves many useful purposes. Its secretion is related to the acid-base balance of the body and is accordingly linked to the kidneys' elimination of an acid urine and to the lungs' blowing off of alkaline gas.

When vomiting becomes protracted, as from an obstructed stomach or intestine, the loss of acid in the gastric juice is reflected in an increased alkalinity of the blood.

The acid nature of the gastric juice is responsible for the destruction of bacteria in the stomach, so that the foodstuffs enter the intestine virtually in a sterile state. Hydrochloric acid also liberates iron from the food and converts it to the form required for absorption. This is an important contribution to red-blood-cell maintenance.

The glands in the lower half of the stomach also secrete an enzyme, which acts upon a member of the vitamin-B complex in food to aid in the absorption and storage in the liver of the vitamin. This vitamin is necessary for the production of the "anti-anemic principle" of the liver, which is required for proper formation of red blood cells in the bone marrow.

One might easily wonder how we can survive the surgical removal of the stomach or a portion of the stomach if its secretions perform so many important functions. Actually, removal of the lower, acid-secreting part of the wall is often performed for relief of stomach or duodenal ulcer, since the acid helps to perpetuate the ulcer. Adjustment to this loss or even to removal of the entire organ can be made, since the intestine is capable of taking over much of the digestive function of the stomach.

When the partly digested food has been liquefied, small quantities at a time are discharged through the contracted ring, the pylorus, which forms the exit of the stomach and the entrance into the small intestine. The liquid food is now called chyme. In part it is a solution and in part an emulsion; that is, finely divided fat globules are dispersed in the liquid. The stomach is eventually empty save for its secretions and, perhaps, swallowed air bubbles.

Proper contractions of the stomach muscles are in some

ways even more important than the processes of chemical digestion. Tense individuals under strain of excitement or anxieties may have spasm of the pylorus, which delays the emptying of the stomach. Or increased rate of spontaneous movement may cause too rapid evacuation of poorly processed chyme into the small intestine. These defects may be the cause of considerable abdominal discomfort which adds further to the woes of the worrier.

The Small Intestine. This long tubular tract (Fig. 29) has three parts, the duodenum, the jejunum, and the ileum, closely related in appearance and behavior. The intestine occupies the greater part of the abdominal cavity in the form of freely movable coils rooted to the back by a sheet of thin mem-

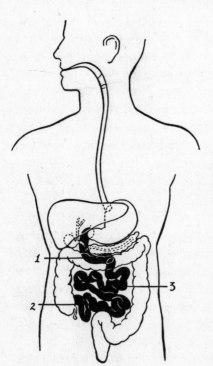

Fig. 29. The small intestine, indicated by dark area. 1. Duodenum. 2. Ileum. 3. Jejunum.

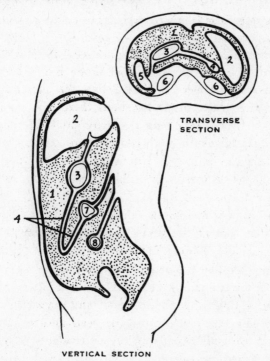

TRANSVERSE SECTION

VERTICAL SECTION

Fig. 30. The course of the peritoneum (heavy black line), showing omentum. 1. Peritoneal cavity (shaded area). 2. Liver. 3. Stomach. 4. Omentum. 5. Spleen. 6. Kidneys. 7. Transverse colon. 8. Small intestine.

branous tissue called the mesentery, which carries the intestine's blood supply. The excursions of intestinal loops can be readily felt through the abdominal wall, especially when they are excessively active. Their motion would not be possible if they were not largely covered by a smooth, moist, delicate membrane, the peritoneum, which lines the entire abdominal cavity (Fig. 30). It envelops most of the liver, the stomach, spleen, jejunum, ileum, and some of the reproductive organs. These organs are said to be within the peritoneal cavity. Others, such as the kidneys, ureter, duodenum, and pancreas, are said to be retroperitoneal because they lie behind the peritoneum. This membrane is comparable to the pleura which covers the lungs and the pericardium which covers the heart. In all situations there is a potential space between the layers lining the body cavity. This may fill up with fluid in people with heart failure or liver disease. The omentum, an apronlike extension of the peritoneum, filled with fat, hangs loosely from the stomach down over the loops of the intestine.

The mucous membrane which lines the small intestine differs from that of the stomach in form and in the character of its glands. Throughout its length there are a series of delicate, fernlike projections into its hollow tube. These projections are called villi (Pl. XII) and consist of a core or stem having a single lymphatic vessel and several minute capillaries. The villi can scarcely be seen and are so numerous and close together that they create a velvety character to the lining. They are covered by a single layer of mucus-secreting cells which forms the only barrier between substances to be absorbed and the capillaries and lymphatics they must enter for dispersion through the body.

The remainder of the wall of the small intestine is composed of two layers of muscle: one encircling the tube, the other running lengthwise. There is continuous spontaneous movement of the intestine in the form of peristaltic waves, which vary in intensity with the distension caused by its contents. If these waves of contraction should cease, we would be in distress from stagnation of the intestinal contents as though there were a true obstruction.

The first part of the small intestine, the duodenum, lies mainly behind the peritoneum. It curves from the pyloric end of the stomach down and then across to the left side again, still above the midline of the abdomen. Its first portion receives the acid chyme and is subject to the development of ulcers like those of the stomach. In its downward portion, the bile from the liver and juice from the pancreas enter, usually through a common opening. Since both are alkaline, the acidity is neutralized, and as a result digestive enzymes from the intestinal wall and the pancreas which require an alkaline medium can be active.

It is in the duodenum that digestion is most active and that the end products are prepared for absorption into the blood and lymph. The digestive juices are contributed in good part by the pancreas (Fig. 31), which in this respect

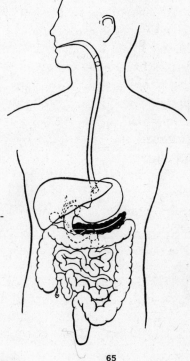

Fig. 31. The pancreas, indicated by dark area.

has a function similar to that of the salivary gland. The pancreas lies in the curve formed by the duodenum and stomach, much as a baby lies in the crook of the arm. The head, or right extremity, of the pancreas is close to the duodenum, and

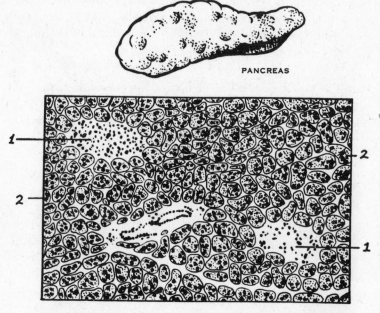

PANCREAS

Fig. 32. The pancreas, whole and in cross section. 1. Insulin-secreting islets of Langerhans. 2. Glands secreting digestive enzymes.

the pancreatic duct enters the intestine at this point (Pl. XII). The tail of the pancreas on the left is near the spleen and left adrenal gland.

The pancreas is really two distinct organs functionally. Scattered through it are nests of cells which, in their activity, bear no relation to the digestive glands. These cells do not connect with a duct, but secrete directly into the blood stream. They are the islets of Langerhans (Fig. 32), noted chiefly for their production of insulin. Since they are related in action to the adrenal, thyroid, and other ductless glands producing hormones, they are discussed in the chapter on endocrines (see page 98). Most of the pancreas's substance, however, is composed of glands lined by a single type of cell which secretes many different powerful digestive enzymes. It is these enzymes which concern us now, as they are active only in the intestinal tract.

When acid chyme reaches the duodenum, a substance called secretin emerges from the duodenum's lining cells and arouses the pancreas to action. The pancreatic secretion into the intestine contains trypsin, which completes the digestion of protein, reducing it to its simplest form, amino acids. Proteolytic enzymes of the intestine are also active in the later stages of protein digestion.

Pancreatic lipases are the most important fat-splitting enzymes in the body. They divide much of the various fats into their two main components: glycerol and fatty acids. Bile salts aid in the digestion and absorption of fat by emulsifying—that is, breaking fat into minute globules for better contact with lipase.

The starch-splitting pancreatic amylase is similar in action to the salivary ptyalin, but more active.

Usually, if the pancreas is surgically removed, or the duct obstructed, digestion can continue well in the intestine since the intestinal glands possess enzymes similar to those of the pancreas. Occasionally, though, if a person has had his pancreas removed it is necessary to replace some of the pancreatic enzymes by pancreatic extracts taken by mouth.

The products of digestion are now ready for absorption as they are propelled through the approximately twenty-four feet of small intestine which constitute the jejunum and ileum. These form the many loops ending in the right lower section of the abdomen at the junction with the large intestine, or colon.

Absorption of digested food readily takes place through the delicate villi that line the small intestine (see page 64). The process occurs much as the absorption of gas proceeds in the lungs. Because there is higher concentration of each substance inside the intestine than in the blood and lymph, a one-way stream into the blood and lymph follows. With few exceptions only the substances in their simplest digested forms are admitted into the blood stream or lymph. Proteins enter as amino acids, fats as fatty acids and glycerol, carbohydrates or starches as simple sugars or monosaccharides. Some are swept into veins draining the intestine, and into the portal vein, a large trunk directly entering the liver.

Absorption into the lymphatic channels is necessary since fatty acids are not water-soluble for admission to the blood. It is believed that combination with bile salts enables the fatty acids to enter the intestinal wall, where they recombine with glycerol and are taken into the lymph. After a fatty meal one can see in the wall of the intestine fat-laden lymph channels which appear like white threads.

Not all absorption can be explained by simple physicochemical laws. It is apparent that the lining cells of the intestine have the ability to participate actively in the selection of material. Simple monosaccharides such as glucose and other sugars are not absorbed at the same rate as long as the lining is intact. In this behavior the intestinal lining cells resemble the lining cells of the kidney tubules. They are not merely passive filters, but perform special work of selective absorption.

Water is also absorbed through the villi as well as in the large intestine. It is interesting to note that it will be absorbed regardless of the state of hydration of the body. Since fluid is being excreted into the intestine in the form of secretions as well, the contents remain liquid until the large intestine is reached.

Inorganic salts are absorbed through the villi by selective action of the lining cells. Calcium and phosphorus for deposit in bone are influenced in their rate of absorption by vitamin D. Iron is absorbed only in inorganic form, so that iron in combination, such as in blood, is not available. Chlorides are readily taken in. Sulfates are not, and therefore have a cathartic effect as they attract water and render the feces more liquid. Many ions such as calcium, phosphorus, magnesium, and iron are also excreted through the intestine and are present in defecated material.

The Large Intestine. The large intestine, or colon (Fig. 33), is about twice the diameter of the small intestine, but its wall

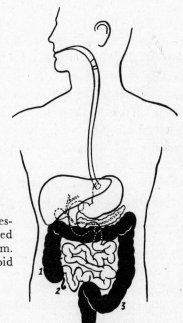

Fig. 33. The large intestine and appendix, indicated by the dark area. 1. Cecum. 2. Appendix. 3. Sigmoid flexure. 4. Rectum.

resembles that of the small intestine in basic layers. Its mucous lining, however, is not in the form of fingerlike villi. Much more mucus is secreted and there are no glands for secreting digestive enzymes.

The site of the first part of the colon, the cecum, is best known because the appendix opens into it close to the junction with the small intestine. The appendix is a wormlike vestigial structure of no use which is frequently obstructed and infected. The colon stretches upward from the right lower corner of the abdomen, and curves just below the liver to course across the upper abdomen as the transverse colon, then descend on the left side to bend into the coils of the sigmoid flexure, and from there join the rectum. The rectum, which is the final unit of the alimentary canal, opens exteriorly at the anal orifice.

By the time the intestinal contents have reached the valve between ileum and colon, absorption of solids is essentially completed. Water is removed from the fecal contents during their passage through the colon, so that they emerge in a formed state unless the colon is too active or too much fluid has entered from the wall.

Bacteria are numerous in the colon and are also found in the terminal part of the small intestine. Their presence is important to the body because of their ability to build up such essential substances as vitamin K, needed for blood coagulation, and several components of vitamin B. At times the continuous taking of antibacterial drugs which sterilize the intestine has resulted in vitamin-K deficiency. On the other hand, colonic bacteria destroy some vitamins such as C, and the degree to which this occurs must be taken into consideration in giving vitamins.

Unless coarse, nondigestible material is eaten in quantity, the fecal material contains little or none of the food. It consists of the bacteria mentioned, substances eliminated through the colon, pus cells or leucocytes, and disintegrating lining tissue. It is commonly accompanied by gas formed in the colon by putrefaction.

The rectum resembles the colon in structure. It contributes more mucus to the feces to facilitate passage through the anal sphincters, those contracting muscle rings which prevent continuous evacuation of the bowel.

Defecation is a voluntary act for which we develop habits in childhood. When the rectum becomes sufficiently distended to initiate the desire to defecate according to our training, contraction of the colonic and rectal wall, powerful voluntary contraction of the abdominal wall, and deep inspiration lowering the diaphragm combine to exert considerable force against the stool. The external anal sphincter simultaneously relaxes and the act is completed.

Passage through the alimentary tract requires a variable amount of time in different individuals and with ingestion of different foods. Intestinal movement is influenced strongly by emotional state. Even well-adjusted individuals recognize variations in the behavior of their gastrointestinal tract in times of stress.

6

THE LIVER is perhaps the most impressive organ in the body in size and in the variety of its activities. As with several other vital organs, such as the kidneys or lungs, the amount of tissue in the liver seems to be superfluous. If need be, we can lose three quarters of our liver cells without a detectable failure of function.

The liver of a healthy young adult weighs about four times as much as his heart or two kidneys. It is enclosed in a smooth membrane like a capsule and is flat, with a rounded dome which fits against the curved diaphragm. Human liver has about the same appearance as beef liver. Since it stores many substances, and converts them into altered forms as well, its size varies with nutrition and age.

The liver (Fig. 34, Pl. IX, Pl. X, and Pl. XII) lies in the upper right quarter of the abdominal cavity and is covered for the most part by the lower ribs. Its left lobe, which is not a distinct division, overlies part of the stomach and the duodenum. The right adrenal gland and the upper pole of the kidney lie against the undersurface of its right lobe. The gallbladder is partly embedded in its midlower expanse near the hilum, where the great vascular trunks enter and the bile ducts drain the liver.

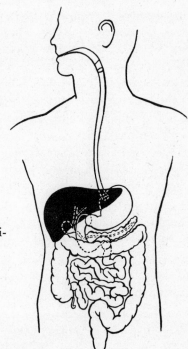

Fig. 34. The liver, indicated by dark area.

There are various ways of describing the structure of the liver, but its pattern is most readily explained in relation to its unique blood supply. The portal venous system, which contributes the greatest quantity of blood to the liver, is a shuttle from the gastrointestinal tract and the spleen and pancreas directly to the liver. All other venous blood in the body returns to the right side of the heart, by way of the venae cavae. The portal blood, carrying products of absorption from the intestine, and iron from the breakdown of blood in the spleen, supplies the liver with a full measure of metabolites for its many duties of synthesis, degradation, and storage. But this blood, being venous, is not sufficiently oxygen-

73

ated and must be joined by blood flowing from the aorta by way of the hepatic artery. These large blood vessels—the portal vein and the hepatic artery—branch through the liver side by side, but as they divide into their finest ramifications their two types of blood mix. Thus the ultimate functioning unit, the cord of liver cells, stretches along a delicate walled sinus, or channel, which contains the richest blood in the body. A series of these sinuses and liver cords converge toward a central lobular vein which, as its name suggests, can be regarded as the center of a functioning group, or lobule. A single lobule of the human liver is about the size of the head of a pin. Its periphery is ill-defined and merges with the borders of adjacent lobules.

The blood drains from the central lobular veins into the main hepatic veins, which join the inferior vena cava. This is the large trunk leading from the abdomen into the right side of the heart. The great vascular bed of the liver is capable of expansion to hold large quantities of blood. When the heart is failing, more blood pools in the congested liver and rapidly increases its size. That is one of the reasons doctors feel for the lower margin of the liver in relation to the ribs. Its size can be judged in part from its location.

The liver plays a major role in the nutrition of the body. It is largely responsible for production of the blood protein, albumin. It is the greatest utilizer of carbohydrates by its manufacture and storage of glycogen, a precursor of blood sugar. As the body requires sugar, it then breaks down the glycogen to glucose. There is also a constant turnover of fat in the liver, where it is received in one form and released in another to be carried to the depots of the body.

The liver is concerned with the clotting of the blood. It is the chief producer of fibrinogen, the plasma protein precursor of the fibrin clot (see page 32). It is the major source of prothrombin, another protein that enters into the coagulation process. The liver cannot form prothrombin unless adequate amounts of the fat-soluble vitamin K are absorbed in the intestine, and fat absorption requires bile salts which the liver manufactures. Conversely, an anticoagulant, heparin, is formed and stored in part in the liver, not by liver cells but by the mast cells which are especially abundant in this organ.

The liver also carries out a myriad of protective activities. It does so by linking some harmful substances with others to form innocuous compounds. It destroys outright some injurious agents. Others it stores, and releases slowly in tolerable quantities.

The liver influences the level of some hormones. For example, the female sex hormone estrogen is destroyed in part by the healthy male liver. Consequently a diseased male liver, failing in this action, may initiate the development of some feminine characteristics in a man.

The liver stores much reserve iron and copper. It is rich in vitamins A and D and has large quantities of vitamin B. It is the body's warehouse for a factor necessary for red-blood-cell formation. It is no wonder that beef and calf's liver, or extracts from them, are excellent food for the anemic and malnourished.

Another essential process is bile formation and excretion by the liver. This allows many waste products to be eliminated into the intestine by way of a duct. At the same time substances required for digestion and absorption are made available to the intestinal contents.

The system which conveys bile through the liver itself follows the same pattern as the liver's blood vessels, but drains in the opposite direction. The smallest biliary unit within a lobule has two liver cords as its wall, so that the liver cell lies in close contact with a nutrient blood capillary on the one hand and its excretory canal, the bile capillary, on the other. At the periphery of the lobule the bile ductules join a larger duct which stems toward the hilum. Here the two main bile ducts emerge alongside the entering portal vein.

Bile is not an entity; it is a complex collection of substances formed partly in the liver and partly by cells of other organs. About 97 per cent of the bile is water. The remainder includes bile pigments, inorganic salts, bile salts, and the lipids lecithin and cholesterol. Bile pigments such as bilirubin result largely from the breakdown of hemoglobin, the red-blood-cell pigment. Special cells in the connective tissues of the body—the reticuloendothelial cells—carry out this breakdown. They are especially active in the spleen and bone marrow. Bilirubin is then carried to the liver in the blood and from there is excreted into the intestine.

Bile salts are produced by the liver cells and are of greatest importance, chiefly for their aid in the digestion and absorption of fats and the fat-soluble vitamins A, D, and K in the intestinal tract. Their work of lowering surface tension in the tract allows the fat droplets to remain as a fine emulsion. The salts are then reabsorbed into the blood and are returned to the liver, where they stimulate further production of bile. A high protein or fat diet enhances bile-salt formation and hence increases the amount of bile. Carbohydrates have the opposite effect.

The substance cholesterol, found in bile, comes from foods, but is also manufactured throughout the body. Bile is not the only means of elimination of cholesterol from the body. Some of it is destroyed, and some is present in breast milk or is lost through the skin.

Bile is continuously being secreted by the liver, although the amount varies with the influence of foodstuffs or drugs.

It is even affected by emotion. Pain and anger suppress its flow. From two to three glassfuls of bile are usually secreted by the liver in twenty-four hours. The bile flows through the ever-enlarging ducts in the liver until it reaches the main hepatic duct outside the organ.

The Biliary Passages. The hepatic duct and the cystic duct, which leads into the gallbladder, form the arms of a Y, with the stem the common duct which enters the first part of the intestine, the duodenum (Pl. XII). The gallbladder is a long, narrow sac resembling an uninflated balloon about as long as the forefinger. It is lined by a mucous membrane and has a thin muscular wall.

The gallbladder performs some useful functions, but is not essential. Many individuals live comfortably after its removal because of stones or infection. Animals such as the horse or the rat lack a gallbladder entirely. In man, bile flows from the liver through the cystic duct into the gallbladder, which stores about one fifth of a cup of bile and releases it into the duodenum at the time it is needed for digestion. During digestion, some bile passes directly from the liver to the duodenum. In the absence of this reservoir, the gallbladder, the bile ducts dilate and hold the continuously secreted bile until it is needed.

In the gallbladder, bile is concentrated about ten times by reabsorption of water and salts into the circulating blood. Some mucus is secreted by the gallbladder wall into the bile but otherwise the bile remains the same.

Physicians can learn about the state of health and activity of the liver and bile passages by examination of the blood, feces, and urine. However, much of the liver must be incapacitated before changes are apparent. If the levels of blood albumin and prothrombin are low and bilirubin pigment is increased, damage to the liver cells has probably occurred. Jaundice, or elevated bilirubin level in the blood, is especially apparent if the bile ducts are completely obstructed, as by a stone. The feces, lacking the yellow bilirubin pigment normally excreted into the intestine, then become the color of clay. Some bile is eliminated into the urine in this case, and can be seen as a yellow foam when the urine is shaken vigorously.

The Kidneys. The two kidneys (Pl. IX and Pl. XIII) lie in the uppermost part of the abdomen behind the peritoneal cavity and alongside the spine. This means that they are separated from the intestines and liver, which lie within the peritoneal cavity. The kidneys have a complete capsule separating them from the surrounding fat and connective tissue which firmly fix the organs in place. The right kidney is situated in part behind the liver. It has an adrenal gland along its upper inner pole and lies close to part of the duodenum and large intestine. The left kidney is usually somewhat higher, since there is no large liver in the way. It is level with the lower two ribs in the rear, although still below the diaphragm. It too is close to an adrenal gland and near the spleen, tail of the pancreas, stomach, and part of the large intestine.

"Kidney shape" has become a common descriptive expression. The shape of a lamb or veal kidney is essentially similar to that of the human organ (Fig. 35). Even the size of the latter is about that of the veal kidney with which we are familiar. The two kidneys together are approximately as large as the heart.

The role of the kidneys as vital functioning organs is to regulate the composition of blood plasma (whole blood with-

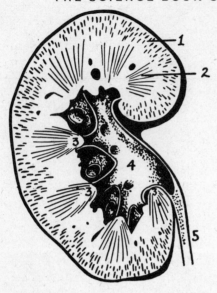

Fig. 35. Cross section of a kidney, showing internal structure. 1. Cortex. 2. Medulla. 3. Papilla. 4. Pelvis. 5. Ureter.

out its cells). By the kidneys' action, the volume of the blood and the level of its many constituents are steadily maintained, despite the constant addition of secretions and waste products and the variations in fluid intake or loss by other means. To carry out their highly important function of elimination and regulation the kidneys must have a constant voluminous blood supply, abundant filtering surfaces, and tubules—small tubes in which the filtered blood plasma is converted into urine.

The main arteries which supply the kidneys are large structures branching directly from the aorta. They divide into very many fine twigs so that the arterial structure within the kidneys resembles a compact bush. About twelve hundred cubic centimeters of blood pass through the kidneys each minute. This is almost one quarter of the output of the heart, and at times the blood flow can be even greater.

The functioning unit of the kidney is a series of closely packed, hollow, threadlike structures called nephrons (Fig.

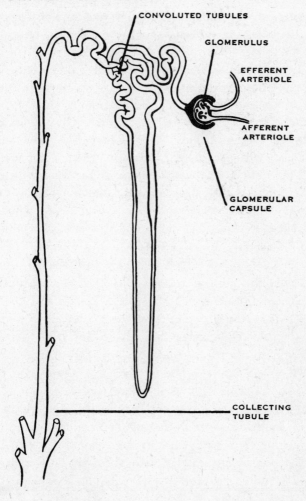

CONVOLUTED TUBULES

GLOMERULUS

EFFERENT ARTERIOLE

AFFERENT ARTERIOLE

GLOMERULAR CAPSULE

COLLECTING TUBULE

Fig. 36. Diagram of a kidney nephron.

36). There are estimated to be about one and one half million of them in each kidney—far more than we need for adequate function. This great number allows for gradual loss of some

81

nephrons due to common diseases. In fact, one kidney can be removed without harm if the other is in a healthy state.

In the outer, or cortical, part of the kidney the nephron begins as a rounded structure, called the glomerulus, which is barely visible to the naked eye. It is composed of several loops of delicate capillaries formed from a single arteriole covered by a double-layered membrane. One layer of the membrane closely envelops the blood vessels. The other is continuous with the long, threadlike part of the nephron called the tubule. The space between the two layers, called the glomerular space, leads directly into the hollow tubule. One can visualize the glomerulus by imagining a closed fist pushed into the side of a lightly inflated balloon. The fingers of the fist roughly resemble the looped capillaries. The walls of the balloon, one of which presses against the fist, simulate the double glomerular capsule. The inner compartment of the balloon represents the glomerular space, and the neck of the balloon the first portion of the tubule.

As the blood circulates through the delicate glomerular capillaries, much of the fluid plasma and its constituents other than protein are filtered into the glomerular space. (The large size of the usual plasma protein prohibits its passage through the intact capillary wall.) This filtration of plasma occurs because of the higher pressure in the blood stream compared with that in the glomerular space and tubule. If the blood pressure within the capillary is too low, as in a condition of shock, fluid will not pass through the membrane. Or if the urinary tract is obstructed, with a consequent rise in its pressure, there comes a point where filtration will cease until the obstruction has been released. The amount of fluid filtered is also influenced indirectly by the pituitary gland, the thyroid and adrenal glands, and by such familiar substances as coffee and alcohol. Any change in the blood flow through the kidney will be reflected in the quantity of fluid passing through the glomerular membrane.

Fluid filtered into the glomerular space naturally drains into the hollow tubule. In the tubule occur the complex readjustments which allow for elimination without a depletion of vital components. The tubular lining cells, by their various activities in different parts, convert the filtered plasma into urine. It is of the utmost importance that the major part of the fluid be returned by the tubule to the blood; otherwise we would be rapidly dehydrated. About four fifths of the water is reabsorbed through the first tortuous or convoluted segment of the tubule regardless of the body's need for conserving water. But in the second, or distal, convoluted tubule the amount of fluid returned to the circulation varies according to the state of hydration of the body. The state of hydration is under the control of a pituitary hormone. When this hormone is not available, large volumes of urine are passed and the individual becomes very thirsty. This is the condition known as diabetes insipidus.

The various constituents of the filtrate in the tubule are altered by active work on the part of the tubular lining cells. Some constituents are completely absorbed by the lining cells. For example, glucose will not appear in the urine unless the amount in the blood is so high that the tubule cannot keep pace in reabsorbing it all. This is the case in untreated diabetes mellitus. Some substances are only partly removed from the filtrate. The tubular lining cells also excrete substances directly into the urine, bypassing the glomerulus. A dye such as phenol red passes through the tubules to appear in the urine, and penicillin is also eliminated in this manner. The mechanism by which each substance is acted upon by the tubule is an individual one, influenced not only by the local state of enzyme activity but also by remote hormone

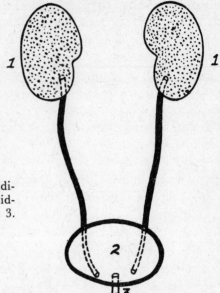

Fig. 37. The ureters, indicated by dark areas. 1. Kidneys. 2. Urinary bladder. 3. Urethra.

control. For example, the adrenal glands are necessary for normal sodium and potassium elimination; and the parathyroid gland influences phosphorus excretion.

In regulating the state of acidity of the blood the kidney tubules perform a most important function. The blood and the glomerular filtrate are normally alkaline. As it passes through the tubule the filtrate becomes acid due to multiple complex mechanisms such as the exchange of a weak base for a strong one, or due to the absorption of bicarbonate.

By the time the fluid has reached the collecting tubules which converge toward the kidney pelvis, the urine is prepared. These collecting tubules form pyramid-shaped projections pointing into the cuplike kidney pelvis. They resemble small teats, and the periodic contraction of a spiral ring of muscle about them milks the urine into the cup.

The Urinary Passages. Each kidney pelvis is connected with the urinary bladder by a hollow thin-walled tube, about the caliber of a pencil, called a ureter (Fig. 37). This tube lies close to the spine throughout its course (Pl. XIII). Urine cannot run down the ureter by gravity, since passage through it must continue even when we are lying down. Urine is moved along by peristalsis—waves of contracting circular muscle similar to those that expel material from the bronchi or the intestine.

The urinary bladder (Pl. XIII and Fig. 38) is a closed sac into whose lower, necklike portion the ureters empty. This organ, the bladder, whose function it is to store urine for periodic release, changes position and shape according to the amount of filling. It ordinarily lies entirely within the pelvic cavity, closely applied to the portion of the bony pelvis direct-

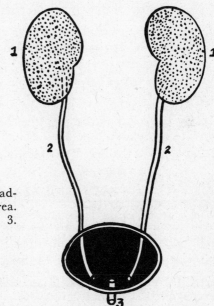

Fig. 38. The urinary bladder indicated by dark area. 1. Kidneys. 2. Ureters. 3. Urethra.

ly in the midfront region (Pl. XIV). In the female the bladder lies between bone and the uterus behind and above it. In the male the seminal vesicles are the only structures between the bladder and the rectum. The peritoneum, that membrane which encloses the abdominal contents, adheres to the top of the bladder, which therefore lies outside the peritoneal cavity along with kidneys, ureters, and some other pelvic organs.

When it is empty, the bladder is flat or concave on top and inclines forward. When it is full, it becomes rounded and projects upward. It is composed of a smooth muscle coat like that of the intestine, but of greater thickness. Its smooth lining is not mucus-producing, but is formed by a compact sheet of epithelium several cells deep. Around the oblique entrance of the ureters the muscle is condensed in such a way as to prevent urine from surging back upward.

The urethra is the tubelike passage which conducts the urine from the bladder to the exterior. It leaves the bladder at its lowermost portion, and with the openings of the ureters forms a triangle near the bladder neck. In the male a ridge of prostatic tissue lies closely applied to this portion of the bladder.

The male urethra, about seven to eight inches long, forms an S-shaped curve from the neck of the bladder through the prostate gland, under the pubic bone to the tip of the penis (Pl. XIV and Fig. 39). Since it conducts semen as well as urine, the ejaculatory ducts empty into it as the urethra traverses the prostate.

The female urethra is short, measuring about one and one half inches in length. It opens into the external genitalia just in front of the opening of the vagina (Pl. XIV). Both the male and female urethrae are lined with epithelium similar to that of the bladder, and there is a thin muscle wall.

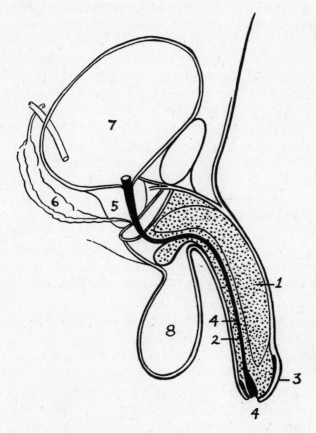

Fig. 39. Cross section of the penis, indicated by shaded area. 1. Corpus cavernosum. 2. Corpus spongiosum. 3. Glans penis. 4. Urethra. 5. Prostate gland. 6. Ejaculatory duct. 7. Urinary bladder. 8. Scrotum.

Urination. In the infant urination is entirely a reflex. Within a short time it can come under voluntary control, but reflexes still play a part. Urine enters the bladder in spurts; and as the sac fills, the tone of the muscular wall builds up pressure. When about a cupful of urine has accumulated, the sensation brings a desire to urinate. The individual voluntarily relaxes the external urethral sphincter, which is voluntary muscle about the lower urethral tract. The internal sphincter, which is involuntary and is formed only by condensation of bladder muscle about the urethral opening, relaxes in turn as a reflex action. Contraction of bladder muscle expels the urine through the relaxed passage. The final emptying of the urethra is due to contraction of muscle in the shaft of the male penis and near the opening of the female vagina.

Intact nerve supply, both sensory and motor, is most important. Spinal injuries or diseases of the pelvic organs may interfere with control of urine even though the urinary tract is itself uninvolved. Even fright can cause loss of control, so delicate is the regulatory mechanism of the urinary tract.

By simple examination of the urine physicians can tell much about the activity of the kidneys. If protein is found, the glomerulus is allowing it through. If sugar is present, it most probably reflects a high blood sugar content. If the urine is too dilute (the specific gravity is low), there is not the proper balance between the amount of fluid filtered through the glomerulus and that reabsorbed through the tubules. If it is alkaline, the tubules are failing to adjust the acidic and basic substances in the filtrate. And if blood cells can be seen when the urine is studied under the microscope, either the glomerulus is allowing their escape or bleeding is occurring in the lower portions of the tract.

8

METABOLISM is a broad term more easily used than defined. The way in which the body utilizes food for the building up of living tissue; the production of energy; and the processes whereby living cells are broken down into simpler substances for re-use or excretion—all these activities are called metabolism. The building up of tissue is called anabolism; the breaking down of tissue, catabolism.

Metabolism properly begins with the food we eat and the air we breathe. The various proteins, fats, carbohydrates, minerals, and vitamins we ingest and the oxygen we inspire provide the raw material from which living tissue is fashioned and energy for its functioning is derived. Proteins, or rather their constituents the amino acids, are the building blocks from which protoplasm is made. The carbohydrates are the fuel whose combustion provides energy. These substances along with oxygen are carried to every cell by the blood stream. All cells contain within them the means to utilize these substances. The means are known as enzyme systems. An enzyme is a complex protein molecule that acts as a biological catalyst—a substance that accelerates chemical changes in its environment. The enzymes' action will be more clearly seen in the following discussion. Not all the cells of the body contain the same kinds of enzymes. The ability of cells and subsequently of organs to specialize in various functions is in large part dependent upon unique enzymes and enzyme systems which allow them to do so. There are, however, enzyme systems that all cells have in common. These are broadly known as the energy-producing enzyme systems.

The Production of Energy. The carbohydrate foods such as the starches and sugars are the chief sources of energy for the human body. These foods are broken down in the gastrointestinal tract and are absorbed by the blood stream as comparatively simple substances. The most important of these simpler compounds is glucose, and by an account of its utilization we shall show how energy is derived.

Glucose is contained in the blood which bathes every cell of the body, and it is actively taken up by these cells. Within the cells glucose undergoes a series of chemical transformations controlled and made possible by a group of enzymes. These enzymes are present in extremely small quantities and, although they take part in the chemical transformations, they are not permanently altered themselves.

Glucose in the presence of oxygen is broken down enzymatically in a series of orderly steps to carbon dioxide, water, and, in the process, to a special energy-containing compound called adenosine triphosphate. In the absence of oxygen, glucose is not broken down to carbon dioxide and water, but to a substance called lactic acid; and, of greater significance, adenosine triphosphate (ATP) is not produced. ATP is the high-energy phosphate compound that makes energy available to cells for heat production, mechanical work such as muscle activity, electrical work such as nerve transmission, and chemical energy for the synthesis of cell protein and other substances. While it is known that ATP provides energy for all these activities, we do not know how the transfer of energy from ATP occurs.

A method of ascertaining an individual's metabolism rate is to estimate the amount of energy his body is producing— an answer arrived at by measuring directly or indirectly his production of heat. When measurement is made under certain standard conditions, the resulting figure is called the basal metabolism rate. Since the amount of oxygen consumed is proportional to the quantity of heat produced, a measure of the oxygen consumed per minute, for from six to eight minutes, can be used to calculate the amount of heat given off. When this rate is correlated with the area of the body surface, the basal metabolic rate is determined. The rate of heat production can be measured directly by placing an individual in a specially constructed tank. The oxygen method, although indirect, is much simpler.

Glucose is not the only substance that can be utilized for energy production. There are glucoselike compounds, amino acids, and fats, which can be acted upon by the energy-producing enzymes for the manufacture of ATP. The food we eat is not the only direct source of energy-producing fuel. During starvation the body's stores of fat and protein are utilized.

The energy-producing enzyme systems of all cells are influenced by potent substances produced elsewhere in the body. Thyroid hormone accelerates all metabolic processes, including the breakdown of glucose. An excess of thyroid hormone so increases the production of energy that the basal metabolic rate is also greatly increased. In cases of thyroid-hormone deficiency the metabolic rate is low. The measuring of the basal metabolic rate is an important diagnostic test for certain types of thyroid disease. Insulin quickly increases the utilization of glucose, for in its absence glucose is not properly used and the excess is excreted in the urine. The adrenocortical hormones tend to slow down the utilization of glucose, but the action of these hormones only seems antagonistic. In reality insulin and adrenocortical hormone act together to provide the body with a fine, sensitive control of its energy production.

Protein Metabolism. The carbohydrate substances, as their name implies, consist of carbon and water. Proteins, however, are characterized by the presence of nitrogen in their structure. Proteins are complex molecules made up of many acids linked together in a very specific fashion. It is the amino acid that contains the nitrogen atom. A few amino acids also contain sulfur atoms.

Within the gastrointestinal tract protein foods such as meat and cheese are broken down to amino acids. Body growth and well-being are dependent upon an adequate supply of certain of these substances. There are twenty-two known amino acids, ten of which are termed essential in the sense that the body cannot make them but must ingest them. The other twelve amino acids can be derived from the ten essential ones or from other substances such as carbohydrates. It is from these comparatively simple chemical compounds, the amino acids, that the proteins of the cell are made.

This building process, or synthesis as biochemists speak of it, is poorly understood. We know that new tissue protein and blood protein must constantly be synthesized, that damaged or wasted tissues must be replaced or repaired, and that normal supplies of protein hormone and enzyme must be maintained. Amino acids may also be taken up by the energy-producing enzymes, and some can be converted into fat. We do not know of specific enzyme systems concerned with the synthesis of the ubiquitous protein products of the mammalian organism, although we are certain they exist. With the recent advent of radioactive isotopes incorporated into amino acids, the fate of these substances in the body is more easily traced.

We know too that certain hormones exert a profound influence over protein synthesis. Growth hormone from the anterior pituitary increases the over-all synthesis of protein. Testosterone, the male sex hormone, causes muscle protein to be made at an increased rate. Thyroid hormone in certain amounts enhances protein synthesis.

Far more specific information is available with regard to the breakdown of proteins than there is concerning their buildup. Muscle protein is broken down to specific end products which may be identified in blood and urine. Those special protein complexes in every mammalian cell which are known as nuclei also give rise to identifiable metabolites (breakdown products). Enzymes in the liver split and degrade some amino acids to urea, which is eventually excreted in the urine. Protein metabolism is a dynamic process. Synthesis and destruction go on side by side. In the growing body, buildup exceeds breakdown; while in the adult body the processes are in equilibrium. It is a sensitive equilibrium, for the scales can easily be tilted in either direction. For convalescence from injury or operation to occur, the balance must be positive. Disease, especially chronic disease, enhances protein breakdown. Although it is convenient to discuss protein metabolism as an isolated phenomenon, in reality it is intimately linked to all other metabolic processes.

Fat Metabolism. One of the principal functions of the fat we take in as food is to provide a large reserve of readily available energy. In addition, the ingested fat serves as a vehicle for the absorption of the essential fat-soluble vitamins. Dietary fat is composed of fatty acids and sterols. Compared to those of glucose and the amino acids, a fatty-acid molecule is quite large. There are twenty-two known fatty acids, of which four are essential.

About 60 per cent of the dietary fatty acids are absorbed by way of the lymphatics of the intestinal mucous membrane. The remaining 40 per cent are absorbed by the intestinal blood vessels and are transported by way of the portal system to the liver. Eventually the fatty acids in the lymphatics are delivered to the blood stream and to the liver, where they are associated with a substance called lecithin, a phosphorus-containing compound, to form a complex termed phospholipid. It is in this form that fatty acids are transported to the tissues. Here they may be burned for energy or stored.

The storage of fat occurs when more is absorbed than can be utilized immediately. Stored, or depot, fat can also be synthesized from carbohydrate which has not been used for energy production. The term "stored fat" does not imply that the fatty acids stored on, for instance, a Monday stay there permanently. Rather, there is constant removal and replacement of the fatty acids of body fat. There is a constant *turnover* of body fat. Little is known concerning the regulation of the turnover rate, but it is well known that during starvation there is an immediate release of fatty acid into the blood stream, where it is available for energy production.

The burning of fatty acids for energy production is generally considered to occur in the liver. The fatty acids are transported to this organ from the fat depots by way of the blood stream. Enzyme systems within the liver break off segments from the large fatty-acid molecules. The segments are then handled by the same energy-producing enzymes that act on the carbohydrates. The burning of fat for energy is not always efficient, as in the case of severe diabetics who must use fat for energy since they cannot utilize carbohydrates for this purpose. In these individuals, parts of the fatty acids are excreted in the urine in the form of ketone bodies.

Although they are not fatty acids, sterols are considered to be fats or, more correctly, lipids. Sterols such as cholesterol are part of a general group of biological compounds called steroids. Cholesterol is present in all animal tissue and in many plants. Aside from cholesterol taken in as food, the human body is capable of synthesizing cholesterol from simple chemical substances. Cholesterol is the source of many of the steroid hormones and of bile acids, and is found throughout the body in various forms.

Water and Electrolyte Metabolism. The first living organism was probably unicellular and developed in the oceans of the Pre-Cambrian Era, well over five hundred million years ago. The concentration of various salts, the quantity of oxygen, and the temperature of those oceans provided a favorable environment for the growth and development of one-cell organisms. The excretion of waste products was a simple matter of ejection into the surrounding water, where they were diluted to insignificance.

The process of evolution is marked by the gradual development of the capacity of living animal organisms to become independent of their surrounding environment. This has been accomplished largely by the literal incorporation of the Pre-Cambrian ocean within the animal body as blood and tissue fluid, called collectively the extracellular body fluid. The function of this fluid is still the same as in Pre-Cambrian times: to provide a consistently favorable internal environment for cell growth and development.

Tissue fluid is held in the interstitial spaces, which are areas between the cells and groups of cells occupied by blood vessels, lymphatics, nerves, and connective tissue. The concentration of various salts is the same in both the blood and tissue fluid. Extracellular fluid contains sodium chloride and bicarbonate predominantly, with some potassium and calcium. These constituents pass freely from the capillaries to the tissue fluid and back. Blood, however, contains substances which are not so freely diffusable, such as the formed elements, red and white cells, and blood (plasma) proteins. In certain abnormal conditions this nice arrangement can be upset, and proteins, red cells, and white cells alone or in combination may diffuse into the tissue fluid. A considerable amount of water and salts is held within the cells proper. The predominant salt within the cells is potassium, accompanied by small quantities of sodium. Since the body salts are capable, when dissolved in water, of conducting an electric current, they are called electrolytes.

Electrolytes and water are absorbed in the gastrointestinal tract and appear in the blood. Shortly thereafter some of the water and salts appear in the tissue fluid. The body normally retains enough water and salts to maintain a fairly specific amount of these substances in the extracellular fluid. The excess is excreted by the kidneys; precisely how is not definitely known. It is known that the hormones of the adrenal cortex and of the posterior pituitary play an important role in controlling the kidneys' action on water and salts. This constancy of the extracellular fluid provides stability for the substances within the cell.

It is into the extracellular fluid that the waste products of cellular metabolism are ejected. These waste products, such as carbon dioxide, are acidic. Carbon dioxide is carried by the blood to the lungs, where it is expired. Nongaseous acidic substances are neutralized by the bicarbonate and other alkaline compounds present in blood. The kidneys excrete other acid wastes and also replenish the blood bicarbonate. For the body to function efficiently the concentration of acid and alkaline substances (the pH) must be very constant; death can result if the extracellular fluid becomes only very slightly too acid or alkaline.

The extracellular fluid is the source of the water and electrolytes found in the gastrointestinal secretions. The normal individual reabsorbs most of this salt and water, but there are diseases in which they are lost by vomiting and diarrhea. Such losses may be so great as to diminish blood volume, concentrate the blood, and cause shock. Other diseases are capable of causing an excess or deficiency of certain electrolytes such as potassium and calcium. In either of these abnormal conditions the heart may be so affected that it can no longer contract efficiently; and if conditions are severe enough it may stop completely. An excess of sodium in the extracellular fluid results in an abnormal deposition of water in the interstitial spaces such that the tissues become waterlogged.

We can see that the simple measurement of these chemicals in a sample of blood taken by a doctor may be important for understanding the condition of a patient with a great variety of disorders. Treatment always takes into consideration the effect of drugs on these metabolic mechanisms.

THE ENDOCRINE GLANDS are organs composed of highly specialized cells—specialized in the sense that they devote themselves to the synthesis of one or more unique chemical substances. These compounds, called hormones, are released directly into the blood stream and are carried to all the cells of the body. Anatomists call the endocrine glands ductless glands or glands of internal secretion. Other glands, such as the salivary glands, have a definite system of channels (ducts), which carry their secretions to specific organs or organ systems—in the case of the salivary glands, the mouth. These ducts do not empty into the blood stream; nor do the secretions of the glands which have ducts exert such widespread and profound influences as the hormones of the ductless glands. The ductless glands such as the adrenal, pituitary, ovaries, testes, parathyroid, thyroid, and certain distinct and separate areas of the pancreas comprise the endocrine system. Their location in the human body is illustrated (Pl. XV).

Within the past decade there has been a tremendous increase in our knowledge concerning the function of the endocrine system. The "facts" and some of the concepts in this field are constantly subject to change and modification as the results of new research are evaluated.

The most valid generalizations that can be made about the endocrine system relate to our ignorance about it. We have only the most elementary knowledge of how the endocrine organs synthesize their unique hormones. Although we have considerable information about the nature of these hormones and their effects upon the body, little is known of *how* they exert these effects. It is a fundamental concept in endocrinology, the study of the ductless glands, that alterations in one gland influence the action of the others. Yet the fullest implications of this observation remain to be explained.

In endocrinology there are three basic types of experiments:

1. The endocrine organ is removed in an experimental animal and the resulting changes, if any, are recorded.

2. An extract is made of the removed organs and injected into the glandless animal. Whatever changes occur in the direction of restoring the animal to normal are observed.

3. A healthy intact animal is given an extract of the gland and again the effects are noted.

Much of our knowledge of the endocrines has also been gleaned from patients suffering with disease of one or two of the endocrine glands. The diseases of the endocrines fall into two types:

1. Those that destroy the gland or impair its function.
2. Those that make it overactive.

Observation of these diseases and their effects is comparable, in a way, to the animal experiments. It should never be forgotten, however, that facts derived from animal experiments do not necessarily hold for human beings. Similarly those data observed in humans may not be applicable to animals. While this holds true for all scientific research, it is particularly true for endocrinology.

Probably the best way to derive a useful understanding of the endocrine glands is to examine their individual units.

The Pituitary Gland. It is appropriate to begin with the pituitary gland, since some of its many hormones directly control the function of the other endocrine organs. The pituitary is located in a bony recess at the base of the skull (Fig. 40).

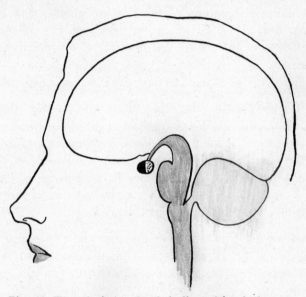

Fig. 40. The pituitary gland, indicated by dark area.

It is small, well supplied with blood vessels, and difficult to remove surgically. Anatomically the pituitary gland is composed of three parts, referred to as anterior, posterior, and middle segments. The anterior and posterior segments are of considerable physiological significance. The functions, if any, of the middle segment are unknown.

The anterior pituitary is often called the master gland. In reality it is a puppet whose secretions are controlled by the brain, other units of the nervous system, and some of the other endocrines.

Modern knowledge of the anterior pituitary began in 1915, with the work of Dr. Philip Smith. He removed the anterior pituitary from rats. The animals died sixty days later. Upon examining the organs of these rats he found the adrenals, thyroid, and gonads (testes in males, ovaries in females) to be much smaller than in normal animals. Histologic examination of these glands and other organs indicated an impairment in the ability of the glands to manufacture hormones. Dr. Smith's experiment has been repeated many times and the results are always the same.

The human counterparts to the experiment are those patients who have diseases which destroy the anterior pituitary. They present the same pictures of gland impairment as do the animals. If an extract of the anterior pituitary is properly prepared and administered, both animals and human patients can be restored to health. In the ensuing years since Dr. Smith first performed his experiment, at least six hormones have been isolated from the crude anterior pituitary extract. Five of these hormones are called *trophic* hormones: adrenocorticotrophin (ACTH), thyrotrophin, and three gonadotrophins. By the word trophic is meant, in this instance, the ability of the hormones to maintain the adrenals, thyroid, and gonads respectively in a state of adequate growth, nutrition, and function. It was the absence of these hormones that gave rise to the findings in Dr. Smith's rats and our patients. The trophic hormones do nothing else but this work of maintenance. Chemically they are all proteins and therefore cannot be given by mouth as they are destroyed by the digestive juices.

The sixth hormone, growth hormone, is also a protein, but not a trophic hormone. Growth hormone, necessary for the normal growth and development of the mammalian body, exerts its influences directly on all organs of the body. Over-production of growth hormone in an adult results in a disease called acromegaly, which is characterized by a generalized enlargement of bony and soft tissues, especially in the arms, legs, and facial structures. In a child, excessive growth hormone produces a giant, all parts of the body growing uniformly. How growth hormone is able to have this effect is unknown.

Anatomically and functionally the posterior area of the pituitary gland is completely different from the anterior segment. In the disease called diabetes insipidus patients drink and urinate tremendous quantities of water: their thirst is unquenchable. (This disease should not be confused with diabetes—that is, diabetes mellitus—wherein the patient excretes sugar in the urine.) When pituitaries of patients with diabetes insipidus were examined, the posterior part was occasionally found to have been destroyed in varying degrees. In other cases, distinct and separate areas of the brain near the posterior pituitary were found to be injured. Two conclusions were drawn from these findings:

1. The posterior pituitary produces a substance that regulates the amount of urine excreted.

2. Distinct areas in the brain may control the secretion of this substance by the posterior pituitary.

These hypotheses have been confirmed experimentally. Again an extract of the posterior pituitary was made and injected into patients suffering from diabetes insipidus. Their symptoms were promptly relieved. The posterior pituitary of rats was removed or destroyed. They developed diabetes insipidus. Distinct areas in the brains of rats were injured. This, too, produced the disease. Finally the posterior pituitary extract was purified and separated into various constituents. Two compounds were isolated: pitressin and pitocin. Pitressin,

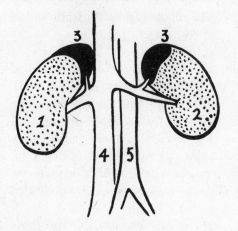

Fig. 41. The adrenal glands, indicated by dark areas. 1. Right kidney. 2. Left kidney. 3. Adrenal glands. 4. Inferior vena cava. 5. Abdominal aorta.

when given to patients with diabetes insipidus, was even more potent than the crude pituitary extract. Pitocin had none of the properties of pitressin. Instead, it was found to initiate labor in a pregnant human and animal. Despite the presence of this powerful substance in the pituitary, there is no evidence to indicate that it plays any role in human labor. However, it is given cautiously by obstetricians to induce labor or to make it more efficient in certain carefully selected cases.

Are there other hormones in the pituitary gland? This is a controversial subject among endocrinologists. Probably not all the hormones of the anterior pituitary have been isolated. Recently several Scandinavian surgeons removed the anterior pituitary in certain cases of cancer, but it is much too early to discuss the results of their procedure.

The Adrenal Glands. Of all the endocrine glands, the adrenal glands are probably the most essential to life. One gland is closely applied to the upper pole of each kidney on either side of the great vessels in the abdomen (Fig. 41). Removal or destruction of both adrenal glands results in death within twenty-four hours.

Our knowledge of the adrenal gland began well over a century ago. Thomas Addison, an English physician, described a disease associated with destruction of the adrenal glands, or suprarenal glands as they are called in Europe. So astute were his observations of the symptoms of this disease, still called Addison's disease, that medical authors today quote him verbatim. It is only in the past twenty years that physicians have been able to present a reasonably adequate explanation of the disease Thomas Addison so clearly described in 1842.

The adrenal gland is a dual organ anatomically and functionally. It consists of a central portion called the medulla and an outer layer called the adrenal cortex. The medulla, which is concerned with the production of adrenalin and adrenalinlike compounds, can be removed in animals with little ill effect. We are not altogether sure that its removal is equally harmless for human beings. However, it is sufficient to say that there are other adrenalin-secreting organs that can supply the body; it is the adrenal cortex that is necessary for life.

The adrenal cortex is under the direct control of the ACTH-secreting anterior pituitary. Ordinarily the cortex produces hormones; but in the absence of ACTH, hormone production in the cortex ceases. There are few metabolic processes in the human being that are not influenced by the adrenocortical hormones. The utilization of sugar and fats for energy and storage purposes is in part controlled by them. The ability of the mammal to maintain a constant body temperature and blood pressure depends in part upon their presence. Without them the human body is unable to withstand the stresses of its internal and external environment. By stress is meant physical and emotional stimuli from any source—for example, exposure to cold, heat, or high altitudes; the taking of examinations; trauma of any sort; and finally, any disease. The hormones of the adrenal cortex not only assist in keeping the body alive in the face of such stimuli, but enable it to meet them efficiently. It is important to bear in mind that such stresses are first apprehended by the nervous system. The nervous system translates these stimuli into impulses which cause a release of ACTH from the pituitary. The released ACTH activates the adrenal gland, which then produces more hormones. In this way the various parts of the body are supplied with adequate adrenocortical hormones.

Chemically the adrenocortical hormones belong to the group of substances classified as steroids. The male and female sex hormones are also steroids, but differ in important chemical constituents. The best available evidence indicates that the human adrenal gland produces a number of steroids. Hydrocortisone (compound F) is secreted in the greatest quantity. Cortisone (compound E), although closely related to compound F, is *not* produced by the human gland. Another hormone, produced in extremely small amounts but of considerable importance, is electrocortin or aldosterone. This compound has recently been isolated. All that is known of it at present is that it has potent effects upon the sodium, potassium, and water metabolism. The adrenal cortex, as well as some of the other endocrine glands, performs feats of chemical synthesis far more complex and intricate than anything chemists can do. We do know that the adrenal cortex is capable of taking extremely simple substances from the blood and manufacturing a complicated steroid hormone.

The cells of the adrenal medulla, the central portion of the gland, produce two closely related substances. The best known is epinephrine (adrenalin). As important, if not more so, is the second, norepinephrine. The pituitary gland does not exercise any control over the secretion of these hormones by the adrenal medulla. Rather, it is the nervous system that directly controls the release of norepinephrine and epinephrine. Epinephrine causes the heart to beat faster and stronger. It also effects a discharge of sugar from the liver into the blood stream, making the sugar available for use as energy. Norepinephrine produces a marked rise in blood pressure without affecting the heart. The impulses of the nervous system that trigger the medulla arise from the same stress stimuli that affect the adrenal cortex. Dr. Cannon many years ago interpreted the action of the hormones produced by the adrenal medulla as preparing the body for "flight or fight." In medical literature this preparatory function has been called the "alarm reaction." The phenomenon is complex and involves interaction between the entire nervous system and many organs of the body. There is also evidence that the epinephrine released by the adrenal medulla causes the anterior pituitary to secrete ACTH and in turn to activate the production of adrenocortical hormone. This is a very attractive hypothesis, for, if it were proven true, it would explain the participation of the adrenal cortex in the stress reaction. However, it is more likely that the nervous impulses that trigger the adrenal medulla also stimulate the anterior pituitary to secrete ACTH.

The Pancreas. The Egyptian "Ebers Papyrus" and a Hindu Sanskrit medical treatise, among the oldest medical writings known, mention a disease characterized by sweet urine and "melting of the flesh." There is no question about the identity of the disease the ancient physicians described. It is diabetes mellitus (sugar diabetes). For centuries the relationship between diabetes and the pancreas was not suspected. This was due, in part, to the structure of the gland.

The pancreas is both a ductless gland and one of external secretion. The bulk of the pancreas consists of cells which pour their secretions into a system of ducts. The smaller ducts carry the secretions to a main duct which fuses with the common bile duct before entering the duodenum. The secretions produced by the aforementioned cells of the pancreas are not hormones, but enzymes. These enzymes act upon food traversing the duodenum, and alter the ingested proteins and carbohydrates in such a way that they may be absorbed. Injury to the enzyme-secreting cells or duct system results in gastrointestinal and nutritional disturbances.

Interspersed among the enzyme-secreting cells of the pancreas are islands of tissue which differ structurally and functionally from their neighbors. These cells (see page 67 and Fig. 32) are called the islets of Langerhans, after the man who first described them. Early in the twentieth century, scientists were able to remove the pancreas of dogs and observe the development of diabetes in the animals so treated. However, closing of the main pancreatic duct did not cause diabetes. Nor were the islets of Langerhans injured by this procedure. It appeared most likely that the islets of Langerhans were functioning as an endocrine organ. Attempts to make an extract of the islet cells and isolate their hormone failed repeatedly. This failure was due to the destruction of the islet-cell hormone, insulin, by the secretions of the enzyme-forming cells. Finally, in 1921, three Canadian scientists, Banting, Best, and Collip, succeeded in isolating insulin.

Insulin is one of the most important regulators of the body's use of sugar. In the absence of insulin the cells of the human organism cannot utilize sugar for energy production with any degree of efficiency. Hence sugar from the diet accumulates in the blood stream and is then excreted in the urine. This is the situation in the diabetic patient. On the other hand, excessive insulin, due either to injection or an islet-cell tumor producing insulin rapidly, lowers the blood sugar. If the blood sugar is lowered too much, coma develops. This coma is called insulin shock.

It is not at all clear how the secretion of insulin is controlled. The anterior pituitary does not secrete a trophic hormone stimulating the islet cells. There is no evidence that the nervous system exerts any control over these cells. Recent evidence indicates that the level of blood sugar may regulate the insulin output. When blood sugar is high, insulin is secreted in greater quantities. When it is low, the production of insulin falls off.

How insulin exerts its effects is comparatively well known. It has a profound effect on several enzymes concerned with the production of energy by the utilization of sugar. In the absence of insulin these enzymes do not perform efficiently. The body then attempts to provide its cells with alternative energy sources. Fats and proteins are broken down at an accelerated rate. The breakdown of body fat releases acids into the blood stream. When sufficient acids are poured into the blood stream the pH of the blood is lowered. This condition is termed acidosis. The lowering of the blood pH is a profound alteration affecting the efficiency of all the cells of the body. Unrelieved acidosis results in death. The administration of insulin and alkaline substances can result in a dramatic improvement of an acidotic patient.

A lack of insulin does not adequately explain all the symptoms of diabetes. Many organs such as the eyes, kidneys, nervous system, and vascular system are injured by this disease. The administration of insulin does not invariably protect against damage to these organs. The removal of the pancreas experimentally in animals and for cancer in humans does not usually result in severe diabetes. The diabetes so induced is fairly mild. Cases have been reported of diabetics suffering from cancer of the pancreas wherein removal of the pancreas ameliorated the diabetes. Diabetes is not a disease whose cause and cure are completely known.

The Gonads. We have come to associate the testes and ovaries almost exclusively with their reproductive functions. While reproduction is unquestionably the most important function of the gonads, the hormones which they produce have far-reaching effects on the body generally.

The testes and ovaries, like some of the other endocrines, are dual organs. Certain distinct cells of the ovaries and testes devote themselves to the production of steroid hormones, while others evolve into spermatozoa and ova. Both functions are closely related and controlled by the gonadotrophins of the anterior pituitary.

The testes are composed of seminiferous tubules in which the spermatozoa mature, and of interstitial epithelium (Leydig cells) which secrete the male hormone testosterone. From birth until puberty there is little activity in any cells of the testes. At puberty the anterior pituitary begins, in some as yet undetermined way, to secrete two gonadotrophins. The first of these, called gametogenic hormone in the male and follicle-stimulating hormone (F.S.H.) in the female, causes the maturation of the spermatozoa in the seminiferous tubules. The second gonadotrophin, interstitial-cell-stimulating hormone (I.C.S.H.), or luteinizing hormone (L.H.) as it is called in women, stimulates the Leydig cells to produce testosterone. With the entrance of testosterone into the blood stream those changes which transform a boy into an adult male begin. Not only do prostate, penis, seminal vesicles, and body hair, which are directly controlled by testosterone, mature, but also other organs and the psyche. Testosterone directs the development of muscle and the maturation of the bony skeleton. Testosterone also assists gametogenic hormone in maintaining spermatogenesis (development of spermatozoa). Throughout adult life the interstitial cells secrete testosterone and the seminiferous tubules produce sperm at a fairly constant rate. At about the fifth or sixth decade of life these functions begin to decrease. The decline is slow and almost imperceptible. There is absolutely no comparison between it and the female menopause.

Ovaries, like the testes, are composed of tissue-producing gametes (ova) and those secreting steroid hormones. The female reproductive cycle is better dealt with in a later chapter (see page 124), even though hormones are its prime mover. However, it is appropriate to mention here the steroid hormones estrogen and progesterone, which have effects other than those related to reproduction. The word estrogen is a noun commonly used. Many substances are classified as estrogens. Some of them are produced by the ovary. Estrogens stimulate the growth and development of the breasts. They speed up the maturation of bones, and as a result the bones cease to grow. This is why women are generally shorter than men. The estrogens influence the deposition of body fat. They may also cause retention of salt and water in the body. Progesterone, aside from its reproductive function, assists in the maturation of breast tissue. It too may cause retention of salt and water.

The Thyroid Gland. The underdeveloped idiot, the cretin, is recognizable throughout human literature. An infant born with no thyroid or a poorly functioning one does not develop mentally or physically. An adult deprived of his thyroid gland does not become an idiot, but all his bodily processes slow down. These two conditions illustrate in brief the role of the thyroid as a regulator of the body's growth, development, and metabolic activity. The gland performs its regulating function by means of an iodine-containing hormone which it produces. Saddle-shaped and about two and one-half inches wide, the thyroid lies across the front of the larynx just above the collarbone (Fig. 42).

THE HEART:

INTERIOR OF·THE LEFT VENTRICLE

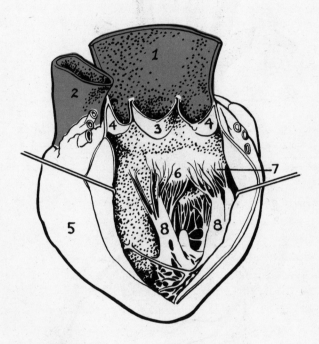

1. Aorta.
2. Pulmonary artery.
3. Posterior cusp of the aortic valve.
4. Right and left anterior cusps of the aortic valve.
5. Right ventricle.
6. Anterior cusp of the mitral valve.
7. Chordae tendineae.
8. Papillary muscles.

PLATE I

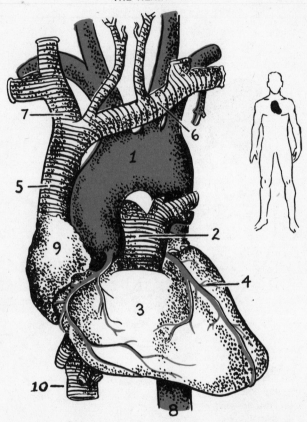

1. Arch of the aorta.
2. Pulmonary artery.
3. Right ventricle.
4. Left ventricle.
5. Superior vena cava.
6. Left innominate vein.
7. Right innominate vein.
8. Thoracic aorta.
9. Right atrium.
10. Inferior vena cava.

PLATE II

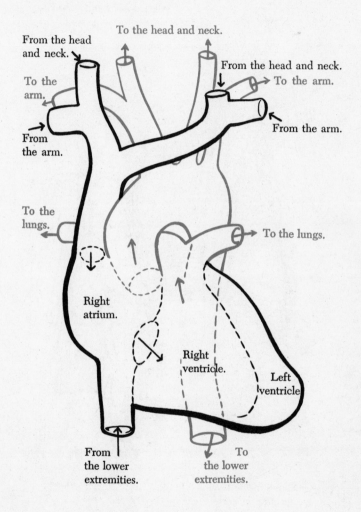

From the head and neck.

To the head and neck.

From the head and neck.

To the arm.

To the arm.

From the arm.

From the arm.

To the lungs.

To the lungs.

Right atrium.

Right ventricle.

Left ventricle

From the lower extremities.

To the lower extremities.

DIAGRAM OF THE HEART

PLATE III

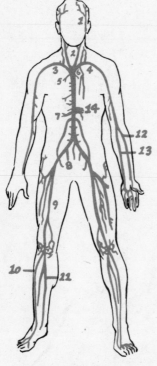

PRINCIPAL ARTERIES.

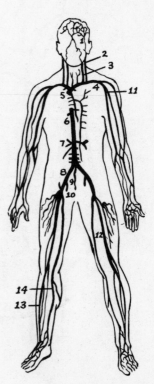

PRINCIPAL VEINS.

*Names of the veins
and arteries are on
the facing page.*

PLATE IV

ARTERIES	VEINS
1. Temporal.	1. Temporal.
2. Common carotid.	2. External jugular.
3. Right subclavian.	3. Internal jugular.
4. Left subclavian.	4. Subclavian.
5. Right coronary.	5. Superior vena cava.
6. Left coronary.	6. Inferior vena cava.
7. Renal.	7. Renal.
8. Hypogastric.	8. Common iliac.
9. Femoral.	9. Middle sacral.
10. Anterior tibial.	10. Hypogastric.
11. Posterior tibial.	11. Brachial.
12. Radius.	12. Femoral.
13. Ulnar.	13. Anterior tibial.
14. Celiac axis.	14. Posterior tibial.

THE PULMONARY CIRCULATORY SYSTEM

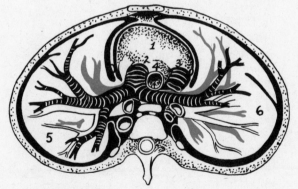

1. Heart.	4. Aorta.
2. Pulmonary artery.	5. Section of left lung.
3. Pulmonary vein.	6. Section of right lung.

PLATE V

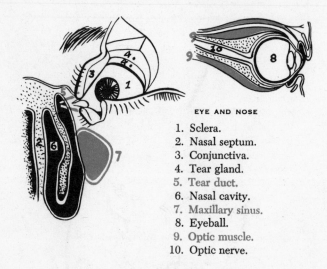

EYE AND NOSE

1. Sclera.
2. Nasal septum.
3. Conjunctiva.
4. Tear gland.
5. Tear duct.
6. Nasal cavity.
7. Maxillary sinus.
8. Eyeball.
9. Optic muscle.
10. Optic nerve.

NOSE AND SINUSES

1. Frontal sinus.
2. Sphenoid sinus.
3. Maxillary sinus.
4. Pharyngeal opening of Eustachian tube.
5. Soft palate.
6. Nasal opening.
7. Nasal cavity.
8. Nasal cavity.

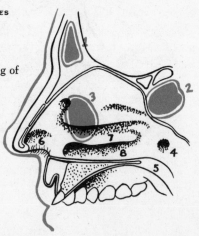

PLATE VI

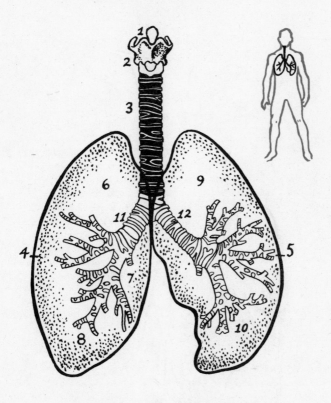

1. Epiglottis.
2. Larynx.
3. Trachea.
4. Right lung.
5. Left lung.
6. Upper lobe.
7. Middle lobe.
8. Lower lobe.
9. Upper lobe.
10. Lower lobe.
11. Right bronchus.
12. Left bronchus.

PLATE VII

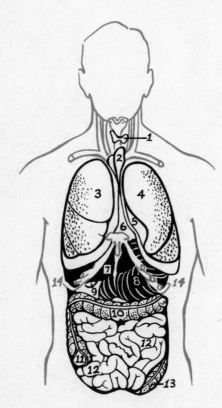

1. Thyroid.
2. Thymus.
3. Right lung.
4. Left lung.
5. Cardiac notch.
6. Pericardium.
7. Liver.
8. Stomach.
9. Gallbladder.
10. Transverse colon.
11. Cecum.
12. Small intestine.
13. Sigmoid flexure.
14. Rib cage.

PLATE VIII

ORGANS OF THE CHEST AND ABDOMEN:

SECOND AND THIRD LAYERS

1. Heart.
2. Liver.
3. Right kidney.
4. Left kidney.
5. Spleen.
6. Gallbladder.
7. Duodenum.
8. Pancreas.
9. Ureter.
10. Urinary bladder.
11. Ascending colon.
12. Appendix.
13. Descending colon.
14. Inferior vena cava.
15. Aorta.

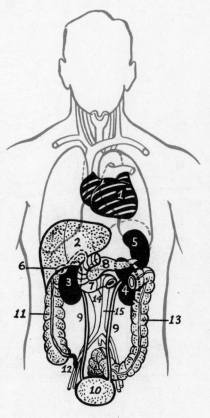

PLATE IX

1. Parotid salivary gland.
2. Sublingual salivary gland.
3. Submaxillary salivary gland.
4. Pharynx.
5. Esophagus.
6. Cardia.
7. Stomach.
8. Pancreas.
9. Liver.
10. Duodenum.
11. Transverse colon.
12. Descending colon.
13. Ascending colon.
14. Appendix.
15. Sigmoid flexure.
16. Rectum.
17. Anus.
18. Gallbladder.
19. Rib cage.

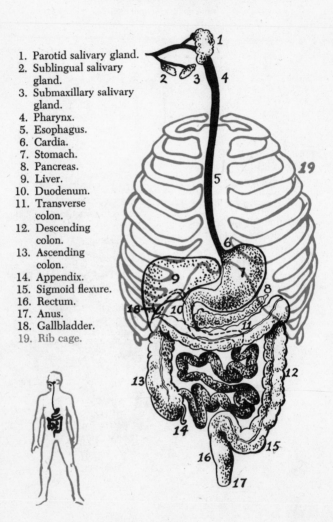

PLATE X

DETAILS OF THE HEAD:
MOUTH AND EAR

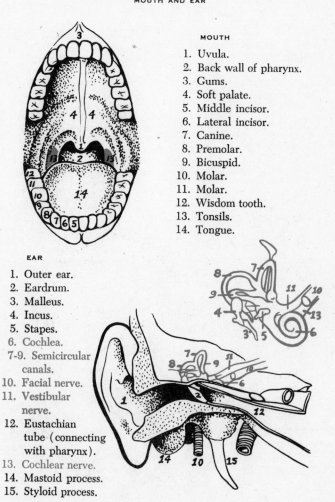

MOUTH

1. Uvula.
2. Back wall of pharynx.
3. Gums.
4. Soft palate.
5. Middle incisor.
6. Lateral incisor.
7. Canine.
8. Premolar.
9. Bicuspid.
10. Molar.
11. Molar.
12. Wisdom tooth.
13. Tonsils.
14. Tongue.

EAR

1. Outer ear.
2. Eardrum.
3. Malleus.
4. Incus.
5. Stapes.
6. Cochlea.
7-9. Semicircular canals.
10. Facial nerve.
11. Vestibular nerve.
12. Eustachian tube (connecting with pharynx).
13. Cochlear nerve.
14. Mastoid process.
15. Styloid process.

PLATE XI

GLANDS

ASSOCIATED WITH THE DIGESTIVE SYSTEM

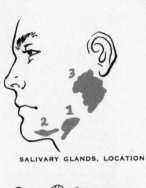

SALIVARY GLANDS, LOCATION

1. Submaxillary gland.
2. Sublingual gland.
3. Parotid gland.

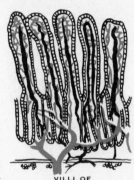

VILLI OF
SMALL INTESTINE

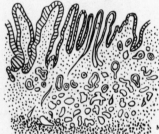

MUCOSA OF STOMACH

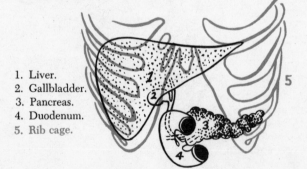

1. Liver.
2. Gallbladder.
3. Pancreas.
4. Duodenum.
5. Rib cage.

PLATE XII

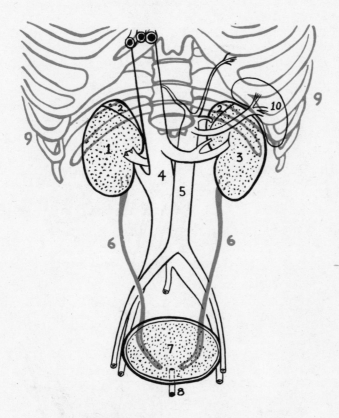

1. Right kidney.
2. Adrenal glands.
3. Left kidney.
4. Inferior vena cava.
5. Aorta.

6. Ureters.
7. Bladder.
8. Urethra.
9. Rib cage.
10. Spleen.

PLATE XIII

THE MALE AND FEMALE URINARY TRACTS
FROM THE BLADDER

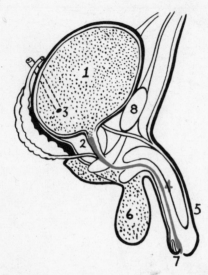

PLATE XIV

THE ENDOCRINE GLANDS

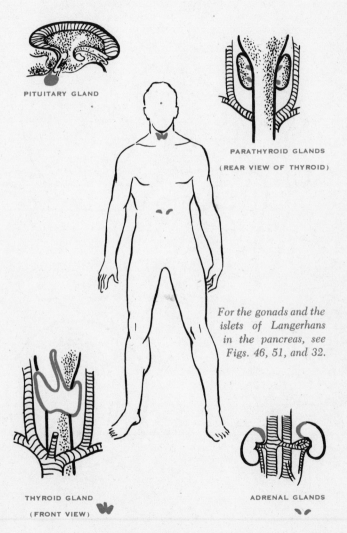

PITUITARY GLAND

PARATHYROID GLANDS

(REAR VIEW OF THYROID)

For the gonads and the islets of Langerhans in the pancreas, see Figs. 46, 51, and 32.

THYROID GLAND

(FRONT VIEW)

ADRENAL GLANDS

PLATE XV

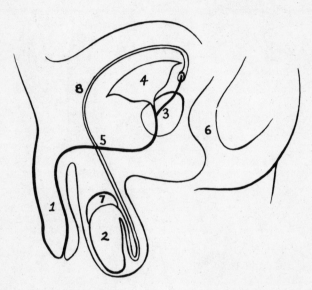

PATH OF SPERMATOZOON

1. Penis.
2. Testis.
3. Prostate gland.
4. Bladder.
5. Urethra.
6. Rectum.
7. Epididymis.
8. Vas deferens.

PLATE XVI

THE FEMALE REPRODUCTIVE SYSTEM

(ANTERIOR-POSTERIOR VIEW)

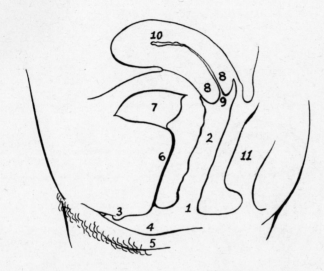

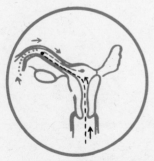

PATHS OF SPERMATOZOON
AND OVUM

1. Orifice of vagina.
2. Vagina.
3. Clitoris.
4. Labium minor.
5. Labium major.
6. Urethra.
7. Bladder.
8. Cervix.
9. External os.
10. Uterus.
11. Rectum.

PLATE XVII

FETUS AND EMBRYO IN THE UTERUS:
VARIOUS STAGES

| 12 DAYS | 21 DAYS | 30 DAYS | 34 DAYS | 6½ WEEKS | 2 MONTHS |

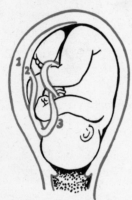

AN ADVANCED FETUS

1. Muscle wall of uterus.
2. Placenta.
3. Umbilical cord.

POSITION OF FETUS, ABOUT THE BEGINNING OF LABOR

1. Rectum.
2. Vagina.

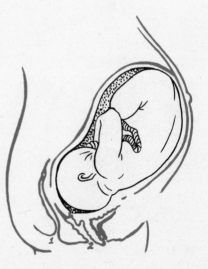

PLATE XVIII

DELIVERY OF AN INFANT

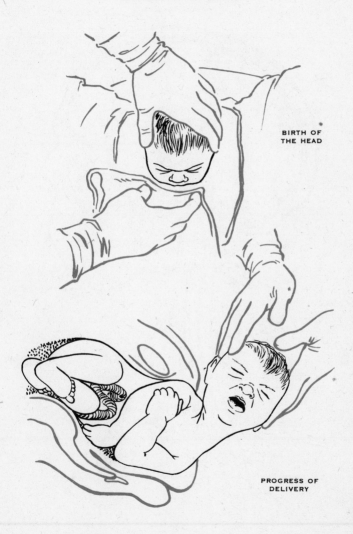

BIRTH OF
THE HEAD

PROGRESS OF
DELIVERY

PLATE XIX

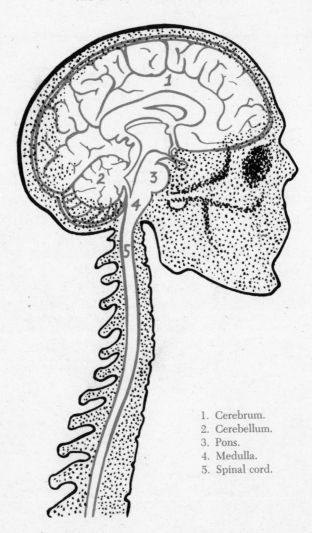

1. Cerebrum.
2. Cerebellum.
3. Pons.
4. Medulla.
5. Spinal cord.

PLATE XX

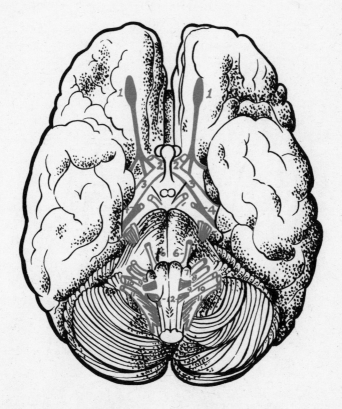

1. Olfactory.   7. Facial.
2. Optic.   8. Acoustic, or auditory.
3. Oculomotor.   9. Glossopharyngeal.
4. Trochlear.   10. Vagus.
5. Trigeminal.   11. Spinal accessory.
6. Abducens.   12. Hypoglossal.

PLATE XXI

THE PERIPHERAL NERVOUS SYSTEM

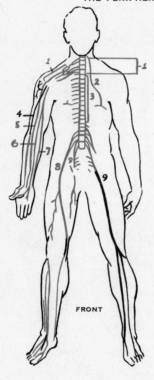

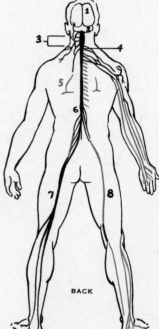

FRONT

1. Brachial plexus.
2. Phrenic nerve.
3. Thoracic nerves.
4. Radial nerve.
5. Musculocutaneous nerve.
6. Median nerve.
7. Ulnar nerve.
8. Femoral nerve.
9. Sciatic nerve.

FRONT

BACK

1. Cerebral hemisphere.
2. Cerebellum.
3. Cervical plexus.
4. Cervical enlargement.
5. Phrenic nerve.
6. Lumbar enlargement.
7. Sciatic nerve.
8. Femoral nerve.

BACK

More than one plane is indicated.
Nerves in red are anterior to those in black.

PLATE XXII

THE BRACHIAL PLEXUS

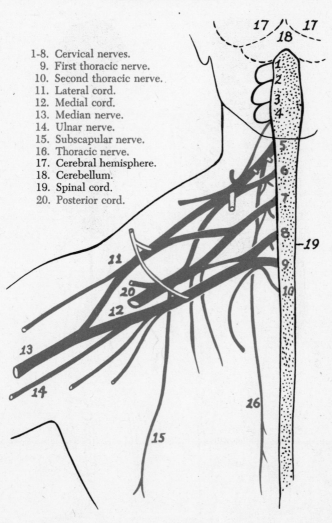

1-8. Cervical nerves.
  9. First thoracic nerve.
10. Second thoracic nerve.
11. Lateral cord.
12. Medial cord.
13. Median nerve.
14. Ulnar nerve.
15. Subscapular nerve.
16. Thoracic nerve.
17. Cerebral hemisphere.
18. Cerebellum.
19. Spinal cord.
20. Posterior cord.

PLATE XXIII

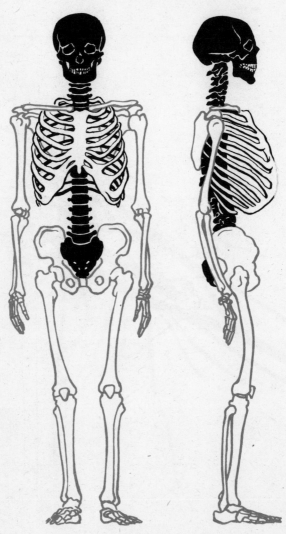

PLATE XXIV

1. Radius.
2. Ulna.

3. Carpus, or wrist.
4. Metacarpus, or palm.
5. Phalanges, or fingers.

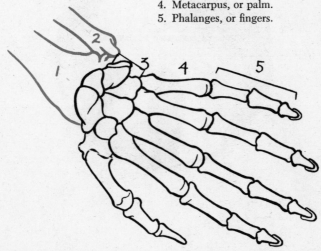

PLATE XXV

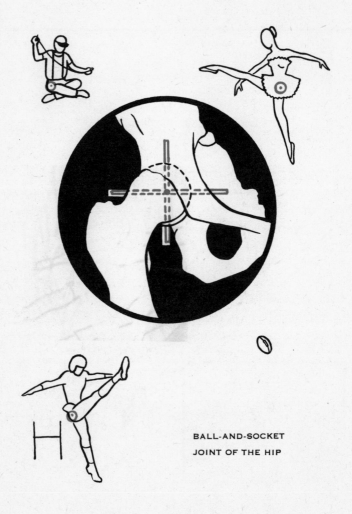

BALL-AND-SOCKET
JOINT OF THE HIP

PLATE XXVI

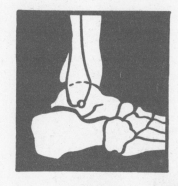
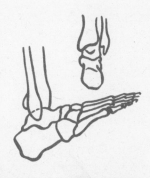

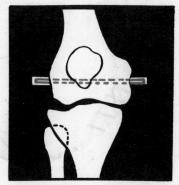

KNEE (FRONT VIEW)

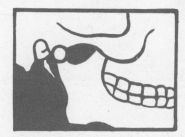

HINGE JOINTS OF THE JAW, KNEE, AND ANKLE

PLATE XXVII

MUSCLES IN ACTION

PLATE XXVIII

MUSCLES IN ACTION

PLATE XXIX

THE MUSCULAR SYSTEM

(FRONT VIEW)

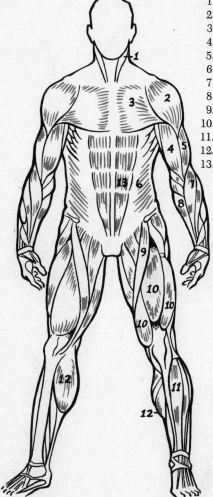

1. Sternocleidomastoid.
2. Deltoid.
3. Pectoralis major.
4. Biceps.
5. Triceps.
6. External oblique.
7. Brachioradialis.
8. Flexor carpi ulnaris.
9. Sartorius.
10. Quadratus femoris.
11. Anterior tibial.
12. Gastrocnemius.
13. Rectus abdominis.

PLATE XXX

THE MUSCULAR SYSTEM

(BACK VIEW)

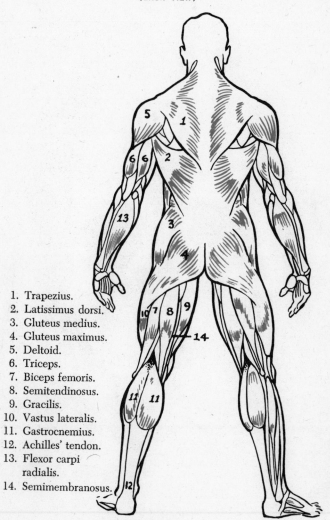

1. Trapezius.
2. Latissimus dorsi.
3. Gluteus medius.
4. Gluteus maximus.
5. Deltoid.
6. Triceps.
7. Biceps femoris.
8. Semitendinosus.
9. Gracilis.
10. Vastus lateralis.
11. Gastrocnemius.
12. Achilles' tendon.
13. Flexor carpi
    radialis.
14. Semimembranosus.

PLATE XXXI

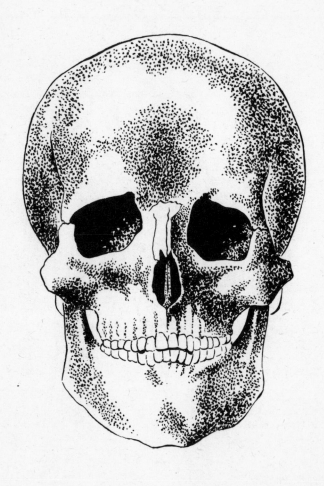

PLATE XXXII

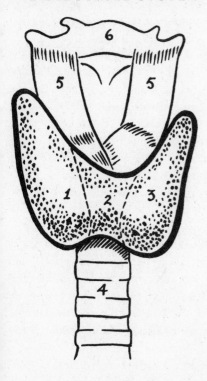

Fig. 42. The thyroid gland (front view). 1. Right lateral lobe. 2. Isthmus. 3. Left lateral lobe. 4. Trachea. 5. Hyothyroid membrane. 6. Hyoid bone.

Among the endocrines the thyroid is unique. Its blood supply is greater than that of any of the other ductless glands. It is capable of storing appreciable quantities of its hormone —something which the other glands cannot do—and it is more susceptible to disease than are the others.

The anterior pituitary, by its secretion of thyrotrophin, regulates the activity of the thyroid and controls the synthesis and release of the thyroid hormone. The anterior pituitary, however, is somewhat of an intermediary between the brain and thyroid. Nervous impulses originating in the brain have a profound effect on the activity of the thyroid gland. Psychic

111

disorders are commonly seen with the development of hyper-thyroidism—that is, overactivity of the thyroid gland.

But if the importance of the anterior pituitary for the thyroid's proper functioning is obvious, its need for iodine is even more so. In the absence of iodine the thyroid can no longer make a potent hormone. Under these circumstances the gland turns out increasing quantities of an iodine-deficient and ineffective substance that enlarges it. This is the origin of so-called simple goiter. There are other goiters whose origins and effects on the body are vastly different.

One kind of goiter, or enlargement, produces an increased amount of *active* thyroid hormone. Patients with overactive thyroids are tense, nervous, sweating, and weak. All of the body's metabolic processes are accelerated. Not only is sugar being more extensively utilized for energy production than normally, but proteins and fats are being broken down and converted to sugar. One of the most injurious effects of excessive thyroid hormone is on the heart. Abnormalities of the heartbeat and heart failure are common occurrences in hyperthyroidism.

We do not definitely know the structure of the thyroid hormone. A substance called thyroxine which has been isolated from the gland is quite potent. However, if the thyroid gland is ground into a fine powder and administered, its action is even more potent. Furthermore, thyroxine cannot always be extracted from the thyroid, yet the powder is active. Recently several synthetic preparations incorporating iodine into the thyroxine compound have been tested. The activity of these compounds is still not as great as that of the powder.

The Parathyroid Glands. In the days when hyperthyroidism was treated by complete removal of the thyroid gland, the patients developed an unusual form of convulsion called tetany. The administration of powdered thyroid gland did

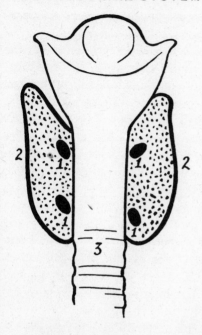

Fig. 43. The parathyroid glands (indicated by dark areas), showing location behind the thyroid gland. 1. Parathyroids. 2. Thyroid (rear view). 3. Trachea.

not affect this disorder. Careful laboratory examination of the blood of patients with tetany revealed a low calcium content. Equally careful anatomical and microscopic examination of the thyroids that had been removed showed that there were included units of tissue definitely not thyroid. Four such units were described, two on each side, behind the thyroid. They were called parathyroids (Fig. 43).

We know now that these bits of tissue are true endocrine glands which have a marked influence on the quantity and utilization of calcium and phosphorus in the human body. Calcium, aside from its importance in bone building, is necessary for the proper functioning of the nervous system. Removal of the parathyroids lowers the level of blood calcium rapidly and results in the abnormal nervous-system functioning manifested as tetany.

The hormone produced by the parathyroids is called para-thormone and can be extracted from the glands in an active form. Overproduction of parathormone, as in a tumor of one or more of the parathyroids, leads to a rise in blood calcium by way of the demineralization of the skeleton. Excessive calcium in the blood may be deposited in other organs, such as the kidneys, and impair their function.

The parathyroids are not controlled by the anterior pituitary. Although it is not certain, it seems as if the levels of blood calcium regulate the activity of the parathyroids. When the blood calcium is high, secretion of parathormone is suppressed. A lowering of the blood calcium stimulates the secretion of parathormone.

Recently a steroid substance, dihydrotachysterol, has been found to mimic the effects of parathormone. This compound is cheaper and easier to administer than protein parathormone.

THE MALE reproductive system (Pl. XVI) consists of those organs that form the spermatozoa, or sex cells, and a passageway with accessory structures that facilitate the entrance of the male sex cells into the female tract. These organs also elaborate hormonal secretions responsible for many of the characteristics we associate with the male. Despite their great importance in the social life of the individual they are not essential for existence. Any part of the tract may be removed or altered by disease without injurious effect on the activity of any vital organ such as the heart or kidneys. The psychological effect of such a change, however, is great.

The Testes. These two structures (Fig. 44), which play a dual role, are essential for reproduction. They are smooth, white, oval, rubbery organs, about the size of a small hen's egg. They ordinarily lie in the scrotum, a free-hanging, thin-walled sac with two compartments. Between the skin and each testis is another delicate sac formed by the extension of the peritoneum down into the scrotum. This is called the tunica vaginalis.

The testes actually develop within the abdominal cavity during the embryonic stage of life. Were they to remain embedded in body warmth, however, development of sex

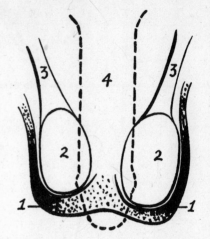

Fig. 44. The scrotum. 1. Scrotum. 2. Testes. 3. Spermatic cord. 4. Penis.

cells would never occur. During late fetal life, or occasionally later, the testes migrate down each side of the groin into the cooler scrotum, forcing the peritoneum ahead of them. If they fail to descend, they are useless for purposes of reproduction and also seem to develop cancers at a higher rate.

The testes are protected only by their position in the scrotum between the upper thighs. Further precaution for their protection must be taken if they are exposed to trauma in vigorous sports.

The testis is the sole site of development of sperm, or spermatozoa, the male sex cells (Fig. 45). These unique cells develop in long, tortuous tubules which can be stretched out like a thread. The tubules are grouped together in incomplete small lobes of conical shape, with their points directed toward the draining ducts (Fig. 46). The spermatozoa-forming cells in their earliest stages make the outer layer of the lining cells. As they mature to become the very much smaller, functioning spermatozoa they progress toward the midportion of the tubule. Along with a little fluid they are

Fig. 45. A single spermatozoon.

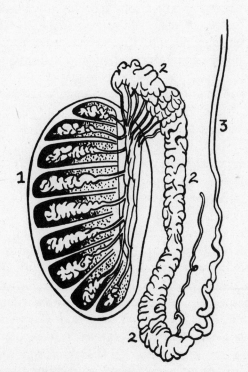

Fig. 46. A testis and epididymis, cross section. 1. Testis.
2. Epididymis. 3. Vas deferens.

then ready to move into collecting tubules and on to the epididymis (see page 119).

The other function of the testis, secretion of the male sex hormone testosterone, has been dealt with in the section on endocrine glands (see page 109). Hormone production is a function of special cells, called Leydig cells, in the supporting tissue between the tubules. But the testis is not the only site of formation of androgens, the male sex hormones. The adrenal glands elaborate in lesser amounts hormones associated with male characteristics.

Sperm are not formed in the testes of a child. During puberty the sperm-forming cells develop and the secondary sex characteristics of beard, lower voice, and muscular and genital development rapidly appear. There is no doubt that they are related to androgen production, since the changes do not occur when the testes are absent. Since there is no abrupt change in the amount of androgens at puberty, perhaps the tissues acted upon by the androgens become more susceptible at that time.

The testes are also responsible for maintenance of male characteristics during youth and middle age. They are not essential for sexual desire, however, and it is even possible for a eunuch, a man devoid of testes, to carry out the sexual act.

A subject of popular interest is the relationship of ageing characteristics and the active functioning of the testes. It is clear that the ageing process, a complicated, little-understood development in all organs, is not correlated with fertility. A sexually vigorous male may show the advanced tissue changes we associate with old age. And conversely a man who appears strong and well preserved may be the nonfertile member of a sterile marriage. This little-recognized fact has led to the erroneous assumption that sterility is more often attributable to the female than to the male.

Temporary inhibition of sperm formation is a frequent occurrence with illnesses in which the temperature rises. Other more lasting causes of the regression of testicular tubules are liver disease, exposure to radiation, or alcoholism. No effect on hormone production, however, accompanies the loss of tubular activity.

The Epididymis. This collection of ducts which lies like a narrow hood along one side of each testis (Fig. 46) stores the spermatozoa and alters their character in an important manner. As they emerge from the testis, sperm cells are full grown. They are smaller than most cells in the body, and have both an ovoid, solid "head," containing the chromosomes for future development, and a long, delicate, whiplike tail for propulsion (Fig. 45). But in the testis they are unable to propel themselves. It is in the epididymis that they gain that ability for spontaneous movement without which sperm cells would never penetrate the inner female reproductive organs to fertilize the egg. When male semen, the fluid produced by the male reproductive organs, is examined in a fertility study, not only are the number and appearance of the spermatozoa noted, but the character of their movement is carefully observed and considered of great importance.

In the first portion, or head, of the epididymis, sperm are moved along by cilia, those waving, hairlike projections of lining cells. Muscle bands about the ducts contract to force the sperm and duct secretions toward the body and tail of the epididymis for temporary storage. From there they pass into the excretory duct, the vas deferens (Fig. 46).

The Spermatic Cord. A cord extends from each epididymis through a canal in the groin. It carries the vas, or ductus, deferens—the continuation of the spermatic channels—with arteries, veins, nerves, lymphatics, and the peritoneal coverings which were drawn down as the testis descended in late fetal life.

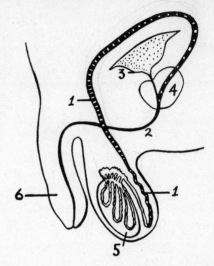

Fig. 47. The vas deferens, showing curving into the body. (Side view.) 1. Vas deferens. 2. Urethra. 3. Urinary bladder. 4. Prostate gland. 5. Testis. 6. Penis.

The vas deferens (Fig. 47) is a thick-walled, cordlike tube with a small passageway. Sperm entering the tube are conveyed up through the region of the groin to the back of the neck of the bladder. Here the vas deferens joins the seminal vesicles to form the ejaculatory ducts (Fig. 48). The latter traverse the prostate and empty into the urethra. Here the urethra is a common conduit for urine and spermatic fluid, or semen. There is no relationship, however, between the urinary and reproductive systems, any more than lungs and stomach are related just because the mouth can conduct both air and food.

The Seminal Vesicles. Behind the neck of the bladder these two convoluted sacs (Fig. 48), which have the contour of old-fashioned water wings, secrete a sticky fluid which forms the bulk of the semen. It is alkaline for protection of the spermatozoa.

The Prostate Gland. This largest accessory male sex structure (Fig. 49) encircles the neck of the urethra as it emerges

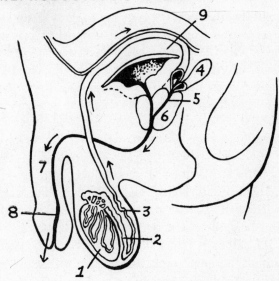

Fig. 48. (Above) The path of spermatozoa from the testis to the exterior (side view of body). 1. Semeniferous tubules of testis. 2. Epididymis. 3. Vas deferens. 4. Seminal vesicles. 5. Ejaculatory duct. 6. Prostate gland. 7. Penis. 8. Urethra. 9. Urinary bladder, partly opened.

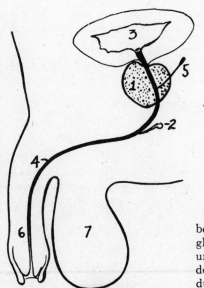

Fig. 49. The prostate and bulbo-urethral glands. 1. Prostate gland (shaded area). 2. Bulbo-urethral gland. 3. Urinary bladder. 4. Urethra. 5. Ejaculatory duct. 6. Penis. 7. Scrotum.

from the bladder. The prostate is a broad, foreshortened, heart-shaped organ, composed of mucus-secreting glands, surrounded by fibromuscular connective tissue. Both glands and tissue are influenced by hormones, and increase in size and number with puberty.

Immediately behind the prostate lies the rectum. It is easy for an examining physician to feel the prostate when he performs a rectal examination with his finger. He can estimate its size and shape, and its consistency tells him something about its inner structure.

The prostate contributes to the sexual function by neutralizing the acid suspension of sperm. This makes the sperm more capable of motion, and the likelihood of fertilization is increased. It is not absolutely essential, however, that the prostate be intact, and because it does not secrete hormones it is relatively dispensable.

Secretions of the prostate collect in several ducts which emerge into the urethra through a common hillock. Secretion is continuous, with periodic excretion into the urine, but during the sexual act more secretion than usual is rapidly formed and forcefully ejected by contraction of the muscular and elastic connective tissues.

The Penis. The bulk of this projection (Fig. 39) is occupied by two long muscular columns of unique structure, the corpora cavernosa. The muscle is traversed by many blood channels. These are ordinarily collapsed, but are capable of rapid filling, an action which results in enlargement of the penis. The firm, erect organ assures the deposition of semen deep in the female tract. Along the back of the penis extends a third smaller muscle column, the corpus spongiosum, which surrounds the urethra. The penis is covered by loose, superfluous skin which allows for considerable variation in its size from the relaxed to the erectile state. In a noncircumcised male this skin covers the firm bulbous cap at the tip, the glans penis. Circumcision removes the redundant foreskin.

Ejaculation. This is essentially a reflex phenomenon which is associated with sensations known as the orgasm. The stimulating impulse arises in the glans penis and results in emission of semen which has been formed by a series of co-ordinated events. Some lubricating glands—the bulbo-urethral glands—discharge into the urethra. The prostatic secretion follows to alkalinize the semen. The seminal vesicles give up their secretion, adding to the bulk of the fluid. Finally the sperm are discharged from the vas deferens and all together pass down the urethra (Fig. 48). All these events are accomplished by contraction of smooth muscle in the various glands and ducts, and they form the emission which may occur even during sleep. Forceful expulsion from the urethra follows a convulsive contraction of voluntary muscle in the penis.

LIKE THOSE of the male, the female reproductive organs must elaborate hormones, produce a special sex cell, and have a clear passageway so that egg and sperm may meet. In addition, the unique function of the female organs is the harboring of fertilized eggs or ova and the nourishment of the growing fetus until it is ready for external existence.

All the organs of the female reproductive system lie in the pelvic cavity, which is the bowl-like concavity formed by the hip bones and the lower end of the spine (Pl. XVII). These organs are not rigidly fixed in place, but have enough flexibility to allow them to extend out of the pelvis into the abdomen during the great enlargement of pregnancy. The peritoneum covers the ovaries, tubes, and upper part of the uterus, but it is then turned back over the bladder in front and the rectum behind. A physician examining his patient from below can feel each organ and estimate its size and contour, except in an obese woman whose organs cannot be reached with the examining finger.

The arrangement of the organs somewhat resembles the pattern of a bat with outstretched wings (Fig. 50). The uterus, the largest organ, represents the body in the midline. The Fallopian tubes are the outstretched arms. Closely applied to the undersurface of the tubes in their outer third lie the ovaries. A thin film of tissue, the broad ligament, spreads out from the uterus to the side walls of the pelvis for support and to encase the ovaries as well as the important blood and nerve supply of the uterus and ovaries. It can be likened to the bat's wings.

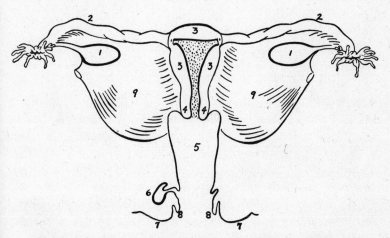

Fig. 50. Cross section of the female reproductive system. 1. Ovaries. 2. Fallopian tubes. 3. Uterus. 4. Cervix. 5. Vagina. 6. Vulvovaginal gland. 7. Labia majora. 8. Labia minora. 9. Broad ligaments.

The structure and behavior of these organs is not uniform, since with the periodic development of the ovum or egg there are marked variations, in the nature of a cycle. These changes are interrelated in the different reproductive organs.

The Ovaries. These two oval structures lie one on either side of the pelvic organs (Fig. 50). In childhood they are smooth and have an opaque white surface. During the time when reproduction is possible, between puberty and menopause, they are about the size of an unshelled almond, with a progressively pitted surface due to the escape of ova. In later years of inactivity they shrivel and have a corrugated surface.

In the female embryo the ovaries are covered by a layer of germinal epithelium. During the embryonic development of the ovary this germinal layer dips into the organ and gives rise to the primitive sex cells, the unripened ova. At birth the ovary has its full complement of ova or eggs—several hundred thousand, of which only some four hundred are destined to ripen during the reproductive years.

The unripened ova lie in a bed of highly cellular connective tissue which is unlike supporting tissue generally in that it is under the influence of the female sex hormones. So far, the ovaries and testes are analogous. Both develop specialized sex cells and elaborate specific hormones which are responsible for the characteristics of the sex. At puberty, in both the male and the female, sex cells begin to mature and are discharged, while hormonal production becomes active. But in the male the maturation of sperm is continuous and abundant. In the female the maturation of ova is periodic and limited. It is convenient to refer to that periodicity as the menstrual cycle, dating it from the onset of one period of bleeding to the onset of the next. This is usually a lapse of from twenty-five to thirty days in most women, although irregularities are very common. We shall follow the parallel changes in each organ during this time.

Beginning at puberty, about the age of thirteen, several ova begin to mature each month, but only one of these usually attains full maturity. This occurs during the first half of the menstrual cycle. The follicle-stimulating hormone of the pituitary (F.S.H.) is responsible for the ripening ovum. As the egg develops, its surrounding germinal or granulosa cells also increase to form the Graafian follicle (Fig. 51), a sac surrounded by special supporting cells, the theca. The ovum remains embedded in a small peninsula at one side of the

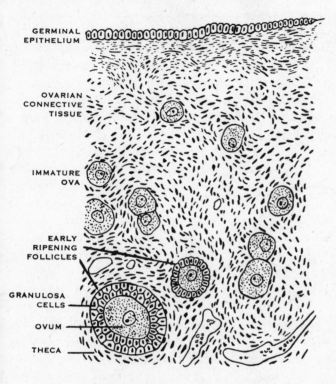

GERMINAL
EPITHELIUM

OVARIAN
CONNECTIVE
TISSUE

IMMATURE
OVA

EARLY
RIPENING
FOLLICLES

GRANULOSA
CELLS

OVUM

THECA

Fig. 51. Microscopic view of the cortex of an ovary, showing Graafian follicles.

wall of this follicle, while the rest develops fluid. Toward the twelfth to the fourteenth day the granulosa cells abruptly increase their production of estrogens, the hormones responsible for feminine characteristics. Then ovulation commonly occurs. The follicle, now visible to the naked eye, ruptures through the surface of the ovary with slight bleeding into the remaining cavity (corpus hemorrhagicum), and the ovum passes into the Fallopian tubes. At times, midperiod discomfort or pain can be related to the follicular rupture.

127

A hormone of the pituitary gland, called the luteinizing hormone, now converts the granulosa cells of the follicle into corpus luteum, a mass of lutein cells which secrete another hormone, progesterone. This hormone is concerned with altering the lining of the uterus in such a way that it becomes a favorable tissue for the embedding of the egg if it should become fertilized. If fertilization does not occur, the corpus luteum degenerates as the follicle-stimulating hormone of the pituitary is starting another cycle. This regression of the corpus luteum into a scar results in the whole pattern of menstrual bleeding and uterine changes to be described in this chapter.

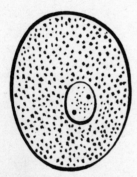

Fig. 52. A mature ovum.

The Fallopian Tubes. These tubes, or ducts (Fig. 50), have a delicate muscle coat and a very intricate inner lining with many interlocking folds. The lining cells are epithelium, with cilia whose wavy motion tends to carry particles toward the uterus. This action of the cilia is necessary, since the egg has no propelling motion of its own. The free end of each tube is funnel-shaped, with a delicate fringe extending outward to receive the ovum (Fig. 52). The movable free extremity covers the ruptured follicle and catches the egg which slowly, for three to six days, is swept toward the uterus. If the tube is obstructed, due to old inflammatory disease and scarring, the egg cannot pass through and the woman may be sterile even though the production of hormones and ova is quite normal. One of the studies carried out to determine why a woman does not become pregnant is to discover whether or not the tubes are open.

The Uterus. This is the organ whose sole function is to care for the developing fetus. It has somewhat the shape of an inverted flattened pear. In its normal position in the body it is tipped forward and overlaps the bladder to some extent (Pl. XVII). This close proximity accounts for the sensation of pressure on the bladder as the uterus enlarges in pregnancy.

The uterus is composed mostly of compact muscle capable of great enlargement and strong contractions during pregnancy. There are always some contractions of the muscular wall. If they are too strong some discomfort may be experienced.

The inner cavity connects with the Fallopian tubes above and the vagina below. The upper two thirds of the uterus are lined by a layer of glandular tissue and special connective tissue which are highly sensitive to hormonal influence. This lining is called the endometrium. It is found only in the body of the uterus, in which a baby can develop. The lower third of the uterus, like a neck projecting into the vagina, is the cervix. The inner cavity of the cervix has many mucus-secreting glands which supply a mucous plug for the cervical canal.

At puberty, when the estrogen secreted in the ovary produces the female sex characteristics of breast development, axillary and genital hair, and enlarging external genital organs, it also acts upon the uterus. Both muscle and the endometrium become thicker, and the cyclic changes in the endometrium which correspond to activity of the ovaries begin.

During the first half of the menstrual cycle, while the ovum is developing, the endometrium grows under the influence of estrogen. In the latter half of the cycle the ovum moves down the tube to the uterus, and the ruptured follicle in the ovary, now a corpus luteum, secretes progesterone. This hormone changes the character of the endometrium to favor the embedding of the ovum. The glands of the endometrium become long and tortuous, with visible secretion. The supporting tissue becomes loose and moist. Many blood vessels develop. If the ovum is not fertilized, it dies. The corpus luteum then regresses, and, with the lack of progesterone to maintain it, the endometrium degenerates and sloughs off, with bleeding which continues several days. This constitutes the menstrual period. The whole cycle then recurs, with repair of the endometrium as another egg matures.

After the menopause, when the hormones decline and the ova no longer mature, the endometrium and muscle coats shrink and are less active. A very common disability developing in the adult uterus is the formation of rounded masses of muscle-forming tumors in the wall. These have nothing to do with cancer, are quite benign, and have to be removed only if they become too large or bleed. These muscle tumors also shrink with the menopause.

The Vagina. The structures described so far are called the internal genital organs. The vagina and vulva constitute the external genital organs. The vagina (Pl. XVII and Fig. 50) is the channel about four inches long which extends upward and toward the back from the exterior between the thighs. It is lined by several layers of epithelium like that of the mouth. The epithelium varies in thickness with different ages.

The cervix of the uterus projects into the upper forward end of the vagina and can readily discharge its contents externally or receive spermatozoa if they are deposited in the vagina. The cervix is protected from trauma by its depth in the body, but it is subjected to the acid secretions in the vagina. As a result, erosions of a superficial nature are very common in the cervix.

The Vulva. The vulva (Fig. 53) is the combination of structures which constitute the visible genital organs. In the adult they are usually covered by two folds of fatty tissue, the labia majora, or large lips. The labia have hair, and there is more hair above and in front of the genitals. The labia minora are two smaller folds which connect in front with a small replica of the male penis called the clitoris. Sexual stimulation results in erection of the clitoris, since it contains smooth muscle with many blood channels, comparable to the erectile tissue of the penis. The clitoris differs from the penis in not transmitting the urethra. The latter belongs to the urinary system and bears no relation to the reproductive organs except in proximity. It opens externally between the clitoris and the vagina.

There are two groups of mucus-secreting glands, one opening on either side of the junction of the vulva and vagina. These serve to lubricate the external genital organs. In a woman who has not had sexual intercourse, the opening into the vaginal tract is partly closed by a membrane called the hymen. The tract must have some opening, however, to allow the escape of menstrual discharge. With intercourse the hymen is ruptured and shrivels away.

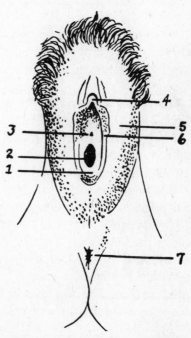

Fig. 53. The vulva. 1. Hymen. 2. Orifice of the vagina. 3. Opening of the urethra. 4. Clitoris. 5. Labium major. 6. Labium minor. 7. Anus.

DURING NORMAL sexual intercourse spermatozoa are projected into the vagina as a result of the male orgasm. It is not necessary for the woman to experience an orgasm for pregnancy to occur.

Many sperm die in the vagina, but some penetrate the cervical canal and, propelled by their own motile tail, make their way up the uterus and into the Fallopian tubes. It is not certain exactly how long the sperm can live, but probably for not more than about a day. If intercourse has not occurred at the time of ovulation there will be no egg to be fertilized and pregnancy is not possible. But if the time is correct and the ovum is in the tube, one sperm may penetrate the capsule of the germ cell (Fig. 54). Then fertilization takes place, usually in the outer half of the tube (Fig. 55).

Within twenty-four hours the fertilized ovum has divided into two cells. The two cells in turn divide and form four. As the cells of the fertilized ovum continue to divide and grow, it descends into the uterus. This process of cell division gives rise to a structure called the blastocyst. About the ninth day after fertilization the blastocyst implants itself on the lining of the uterus (Fig. 55). The blastocyst's outer rim of cells burrows into the rich uterine lining which has been built up

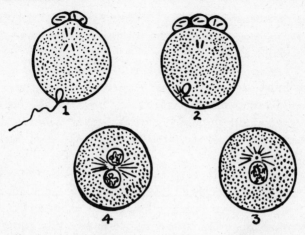

Fig. 54. Fertilization of an ovum by a spermatozoon.

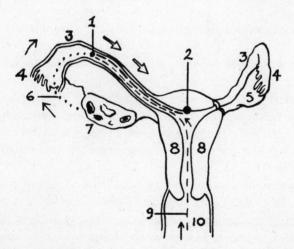

Fig. 55. Fallopian tube, uterus, vagina, and meeting place of spermatozoon and ovum. 1. Site of fertilization in Fallopian tube. 2. Site of implantation of fertilized ovum. 3. Fallopian tubes. 4. Fimbriated end of Fallopian tubes. 5. Ovary. 6. Path of ovum. 7. Ruptured follicle of ovary. 8. Uterus. 9. Path of spermatozoon. 10. Vagina.

during the menstrual cycle. These cells, called trophoblasts, actively secrete chorionic gonadotrophin, a hormone which in turn maintains the secretion of estrogens and progesterone by the corpus luteum. The latter does not regress and the uterine lining is not disrupted. Menstruation therefore ceases for the duration of pregnancy. The presence of chorionic gonadotrophin in the urine of a pregnant woman can be detected at this early stage by the commonly used Ascheim-Zondek test.

The burrowing process carried on by the trophoblasts brings the fertilized egg into contact with the abundant blood supply of the maternal uterine lining, now called the decidua. The trophoblasts grow rapidly and form fingerlike projections which erode their way into the maternal uterine blood supply. At this early period of life the embryo is nourished by food substances passing from the maternal blood across these fingerlike projections, called villi. The villi are forerunners of the developing placenta. Three weeks after conception, blood vessels develop in the villi, and one month later these vessels fuse to form the umbilical artery and vein. The inner cell mass of the ovum grows very rapidly and by the hundredth day the fetus and the round flat organ called the placenta are well developed. The placenta establishes communication between mother and child by means of the umbilical artery and vein (Pl. XVIII).

The umbilical vein carries the fetal blood to the placenta, where the fetal waste products diffuse across the placental membrane into the maternal blood. Various food substances, electrolytes, water, and minerals diffuse from the maternal blood across the placental membrane and are eventually carried to the fetus by the umbilical artery. In addition to its transportation duties the placenta produces estrogens and progesterone, which play a major role in maintaining the uterine lining so that it can support the life of the fetus. The

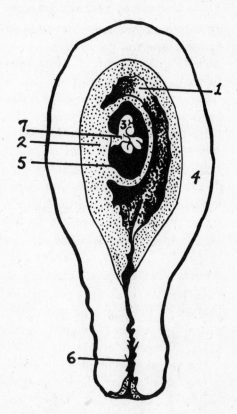

Fig. 56. The embryo in the uterus, showing its point of attachment. 1. Uterine cavity. 2. Placenta. 3. Embryo. 4. Uterine muscle wall. 5. Amniotic sac. 6. Cervical canal. 7. Umbilical cord.

placenta, at this stage of its growth, no longer produces chorionic gonadotrophin.

No nerves traverse the placenta and umbilical cord, so that connection between the nervous system of mother and child does not exist. Prenatal influence, then, is limited to nutrition, which the fetus obtains from the mother. Nervous or emotional influence cannot occur other than as emotions affect the behavior and well-being of the mother.

As the ovum develops, two sacs form within the trophoblast: the amniotic sac and the yolk sac. The amniotic sac (Fig. 56) is small at first, but accumulates fluid throughout

135

pregnancy. Eventually the fetus is surrounded by from a pint to a quart of clear, light yellow fluid. The amount varies at times, however, from a tablespoon to several quarts. The yolk sac, which is more prominent at the beginning of pregnancy, eventually gives rise to much of the intestinal tract of the fetus and disappears in later development.

The Development of the Baby. It requires about nine calendar months, ten lunar months, or 275 to 280 days for complete development of the infant. During the first half of pregnancy, growth in size is most striking, but differentiation into special organs with specific cell functions is occurring. In the latter part of pregnancy, maturing of each special cell progresses, and increase in size is a less prominent aspect of the growth activity.

Students of the process of differentiation into special cells with specific functions have determined just which spot is destined to become a particular structure. This was accomplished by performing delicate operations on developing animal embryos and noting the altered pattern thus produced.

The sex of the infant is determined early—as a matter of fact, as soon as fertilization of the ovum has occurred—and there is no possibility of a true change. The developing primitive sperm cell in the male testis contains two kinds of sex chromosomes designated as X and Y. As the developing sperm cell divides, some spermatozoa receive the X type of chromosomes, some the Y. The female ovum contains only the X type. If the particular sperm fertilizing the egg has an X, the double-X combination results in a female child. The Y-containing sperm will join with the X-containing ovum to form the male X-Y combination. Thus it is clear that there is nothing at all the mother can do to influence the sex of her child. Sex depends entirely on which one of the very many available sperm happens to penetrate the egg.

The developing structure in the uterus is called the embryo while various organs are undergoing initial formation from the third to the eighth week (Pl. XVIII). At the eighth week the human fetus, as it is known from this point on, resembles the fetus of other mammals. It is curved forward so that the forehead and tail almost touch. In the human the head and brain show an early disproportionate enlargement and the limbs are short. Proper proportions are gradually assumed, so that the newborn infant essentially resembles man in structure.

During fetal life certain differences of structure necessarily exist for adaptation to the uterine life. For example, since the fetus cannot breathe there is no need for most of the blood to pass through its lungs. Much is bypassed from the right to the left side of the heart through an opening in the wall between them and through a connection between the pulmonary artery and the aorta. These connections should close after birth, when the infant's blood must pass through the lungs. A "blue baby" is one whose blood is not well oxygenated because such a prenatal connection did not disappear. A surgeon experienced in this particular work can correct the defect.

Most commonly the fetus lies in the uterus with head down, arms folded, knees drawn high, and feet crossed (Fig. 57). Many other positions are possible, however. To determine the position, the examining physician can feel various structures such as head and foot, and can listen to the location of the fetal heartbeat after the fourth month. Ample fluid in the amniotic sac allows the fetus to move spontaneously and give little kicks of which the mother is aware after the fifth month. It is also possible for the fetus to be manipulated into an optimal position for delivery, but babies are delivered successfully even when the buttocks appear first, as in a so-called breech presentation.

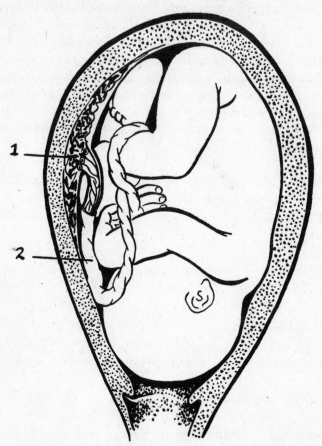

Fig. 57. The uterus containing a fetus. 1. Placenta. 2. Umbilical cord.

The mother's body must alter in many ways to accommodate and nourish the growing fetus. The uterine wall becomes markedly thickened and stretched, partly under hormonal influence and partly because stretching of its muscle by the fetus causes each fiber to become thicker and longer. Early

138

in pregnancy the uterus presses on the bladder, but as it rises out of the pelvis the more distensible abdominal cavity carries the enlarging fetus until late in pregnancy. If there is great enlargement and other organs are crowded, pressure on the diaphragm and hence on the lungs may cause some difficulty in breathing. In the final days of pregnancy, as the head of the fetus settles down into the pelvis (Pl. XVIII), there is respiratory relief, but again the bladder cannot expand as readily.

Carrying a child has no injurious effect on a mother, if she eats and rests well. If she does not, she may become anemic. Contrary to popular belief, dental caries, or cavities, are not produced by pregnancy. However, the gums may become temporarily swollen from hormonal effect. The skin is apt to develop brown spots, and small groups of dilated blood vessels may appear.

The Mammary Glands. Aside from growth of the uterus, the greatest alteration during pregnancy occurs in the breasts, or mammary glands (Fig. 58). These structures—in the human

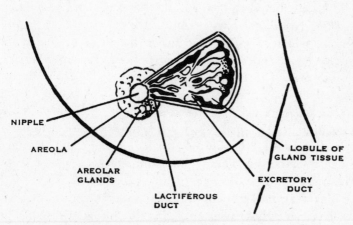

NIPPLE

AREOLA

AREOLAR
GLANDS

LACTIFEROUS
DUCT

LOBULE OF
GLAND TISSUE

EXCRETORY
DUCT

Fig. 58. Diagram of the breast, or mammary gland.

normally only two, one on either side of the front of the chest—are really modified sweat glands. Before puberty they are rudimentary, like those of the male. They consist of from ten to twenty branching ducts in a dense supporting tissue. The ducts open into the nipple, a rounded pink structure with muscle fibers capable of contraction. Under stimulus the nipple thus undergoes erection. The areola forms a light pink border around the nipple.

With puberty, the mammary gland tissue of the female increases as ovarian hormones are released. The rounded contour, however, owes its configuration to fat which forms around and among the glandular lobules. The breasts are still soft and compressible, but are supported by suspensory ligaments which keep them from becoming pendulous.

As pregnancy advances, the breasts enlarge further and are ready to assume their only function, that of producing milk for the infant. Groups of glands called alveoli sprout from ducts and form compact glandular tissue. More blood vessels appear and tissue fluid increases. The breasts become firm and more rounded. The nipples turn darker. These changes can be attributed to ovarian and placental hormone activity.

Birth. No one knows exactly why gestation, the period during which the baby remains in the body of the mother, comes to an end and the infant is born. Perhaps there is a withdrawal of ovarian hormones which reduces the restraining effect upon uterine contractions. Perhaps ageing changes in the placenta alter the blood supply to the infant. Perhaps size stretches the wall to a point where stronger contractions are stimulated. Probably no one factor alone initiates labor, since it can occur at any time during the development of the baby.

It is very rare for a fetus born before the seventh month to live. Even those who are delivered during the eighth and ninth lunar months require extra care. Since they have not attained maturity they still resemble a fetus, with a relatively large head and wrinkled red skin like that of a little old man. An infant born prematurely has a better chance of survival in the controlled atmosphere of an incubator and with careful hand feeding, since his muscles are weak and his reflexes are not well co-ordinated.

Labor, or childbirth, begins with stronger than usual uterine contractions, now painful and accompanied by dilation of the cervix. This first stage lasts a variable period of time, but commonly longer with the first child. The bag of waters, or amniotic sac, ruptures, and with each pain the fluid is expelled.

The second stage of labor is the actual expulsion of the child. It also varies greatly in the length of time required. The average period lasts from one to two hours. The head most often makes its appearance first, and the shoulders, body, and legs follow with each forceful contraction (Pl. XIX). In an uncomplicated delivery the obstetrician's role is one of guidance, support, and prevention of tearing. The mother involuntarily expels the child.

The umbilical cord, still connecting child and placenta, now protrudes from the vagina. It is clamped and cut. The newborn infant may breathe spontaneously when the head is delivered. Upon complete delivery he is suspended by his feet to allow secretions to run out of his mouth and nose. A lusty cry is promptly encouraged to expand his lungs and chest.

The baby commonly appears quite grotesque. The head has been molded in its passage through the pelvis. He is covered with a cheesy material called the vernix, and his face appears congested and full. Immediate care calls for a sterile dressing over the umbilical cord and silver nitrate in the eyes to prevent infection. He is wiped with soft cotton, wrapped warmly, and laid on a flat firm bed.

The third stage of labor should proceed immediately. This entails spontaneous separation of the placenta, and its expulsion from the uterus. The placenta may be forced through the vagina by voluntary abdominal contractions, or the physician may aid its further removal. It is most important that the placenta be inspected for completeness, since remnants in the uterus are apt to bleed. Excessive hemorrhage may also occur if the uterus becomes too relaxed. It should be watched, and massaged if need be during the critical hour following placental delivery.

During the puerperium, or six weeks of recovery after childbirth, the uterus gradually regresses, but remains a little larger than it was before pregnancy. Discharge from the vagina persists for about two weeks. If the mother is not nursing her child, the menstrual cycle and ovulation will be resumed earlier than otherwise—often when the baby is from about six to eight weeks old. Many women believe that they cannot become pregnant while they are lactating, but this has been disproved frequently. If a child is nursed continuously, the menstrual flow appears anywhere from six months to a year and a half after delivery.

Lactation, or the formation of milk, begins at about the time of delivery. For the first few days only a thin, yellowish fluid, the colostrum, can be expressed. It has little nutritional value and contains chiefly protein and salts, with little fat. Production of milk begins about the third or fourth day after delivery. Estrogen of the ovaries was required for growth of the mammary gland during pregnancy, but it does not initiate lactation. In fact, estrogen inhibits the liberation of lactogenic hormone by the pituitary. Hence, when estrogen production is diminished with childbirth, lactogen, the milk-stimulating pituitary hormone, becomes effective. Mother's milk is of high nutritive value. Most physicians urge that the child nurse from the mother when possible.

THE NERVOUS SYSTEM is probably the most important means by which the human organism is integrated and enabled to function as a whole. Because of it the body can react to its environment, both external and internal. The nervous system is, in a way, a communication system between the organs that come in contact with the outside environment—such as the skin, the eyes, the ears, the tongue—and a central switchboard called the brain, where decisions are made so that the body can react adequately to different situations. These decisions are then transmitted by way of various parts of the communication system to the organs that will perform the appropriate actions. The internal environment—the internal organs and the situations that confront them, such as breathing, blood circulation, food digestion, and waste elimination—is also regulated by parts of the nervous system. Although these function at a somewhat different level, called the reflex level, they too act by way of the ramifications of the complex network we call the nervous system.

It is difficult to comprehend the nervous system as a whole unless its anatomical and functional subdivisions are first understood. Even then, one must remember that these subdivisions are arbitrary and man-made. The nervous system

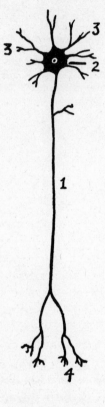

Fig. 59. Diagram of a motor neuron. 1. Axon. 2. Cell body. 3. Dendrites. 4. Nerve endings.

functions as a unit in the same way as does any other complex mechanism.

The basic cell of the nervous system is the nerve cell, called a neuron. This type of cell differs from other cells in the body in several ways. Probably the most important way, in terms of disease and injury, is that the neuron does not replace itself. At birth the human body contains all the nerve cells it will ever have. When a nerve cell is destroyed, no new neuron is produced to take its place.

Each neuron is characterized by the fact that it sends out a single long appendage, or process, which may extend as far as two or three feet (Fig. 59). This long process, actually a continuation of the cell body, is called the axon. In addition to the axon there are, on each neuron, a variable number of much shorter processes called dendrites. All these processes have the property of the nerve cell which is not shared by most other cells of the human body: that of transmitting electrical impulses. The dendrites transmit impulses *to* the cell, while the axon transmits impulses *from* the cell. Thus it is possible, when examining the nervous system under the microscope, to tell from the direction of the axon whether the cell transmits *to* the brain from the organs or *from* the brain to the organs.

Few cells transmit impulses directly from the brain to the organs. In most instances other nerve cells are employed

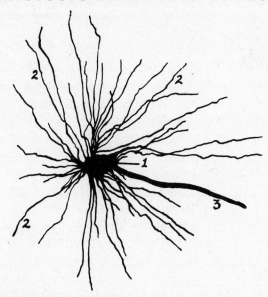

Fig. 60. A nerve cell of the cerebral cortex. 1. Cell body. 2. Dendrites. 3. Axon.

as relay stations. Here we come upon another peculiarity of the nervous system: there are no direct connections between the nerve cells. The axon of one neuron lies close to, but not attached to, the dendrites of another nerve cell. The gap between them is called the synapse. Most authorities believe that the nerve impulse bridges the synapse by a complex and almost instantaneous chemical reaction which is helped by certain highly specific enzymes.

It is useful to divide the system into two main subdivisions: the central nervous system, which consists of the brain and the spinal cord; and the peripheral nervous system, which is comprised of the cranial nerves, the spinal roots, and the nerve trunks. The nervous system's network consists of nerve cells and their intertwining dendrites and axons (Fig. 60). In

Fig. 61. Diagram of a sensory neuron. 1. Ganglion cell.

certain areas of the system there exist groups of nerve cells called nuclei. When these groups of cells are found outside the brain and spinal cord they are called ganglia (Fig. 61).

In addition to the nerve cells and their processes there are supporting cells in the nervous system. These are the equivalent of the connective-tissue cells found in every other organ, but here they have a special name and are called glia. The glia and the blood vessels, which of course pervade the substance of the brain and spinal cord, give the brain and cord their characteristic shape. They are the beams and the walls that house the delicate nervous-system network.

The axons of the nerve cells are surrounded by a sheath of fatty material called myelin. This sheath has a whitish color. The nerve cells and glia, on the other hand, do not have such a sheath. When the brain or the spinal cord are examined with the naked eye, one can easily see that certain areas are grayish. They are the so-called gray matter which contains almost all the nerve-cell bodies—that is, the neurons proper. Other areas appear to be white—the so-called white matter. The latter contains the axons with their myelin sheath (Fig. 62). Axons are commonly grouped together to form bundles. Such bundles are called tracts, or columns, when they are found within the substance of the brain or spinal cord, and nerves, or nerve trunks, when they leave the spinal cord or the brain to go to the several organs.

The nervous system has two great functions, one sensory, one motor.

The brain can be regarded as a switchboard that receives impulses from the outside—that is, the outside world or the internal organs; takes action upon this information which has been brought in by sensory nerves to sensory neurons and to the brain by sensory tracts; and then sends out its "decision for action." These actions originate in motor neurons; travel by way of motor tracts; and are brought to the limbs or the appropriate internal organ by way of motor nerves.

In some cases the information brought in by the sensory neurons does not require very elaborate "consideration," and action can be taken almost immediately without referral to what have been called the higher centers located in the brain. Such action is called reflex, and takes place in the

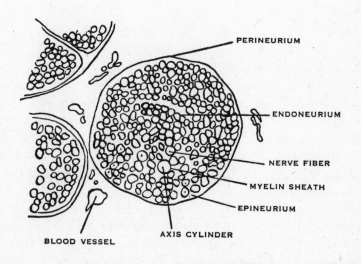

Fig. 62. Cross section of a peripheral nerve.

spinal cord (Fig. 63) or in reflex centers located in different parts of the brain.

The nervous system has been divided into two functional subdivisions: the autonomic and the somatic nervous systems. The autonomic nervous system is concerned almost exclusively with such reflex functions as the heartbeat, respiration, gastrointestinal motility, bladder function, and sweating. It is. the older system in the scale of evolution. It is therefore easy to understand that the nervous centers for the above-

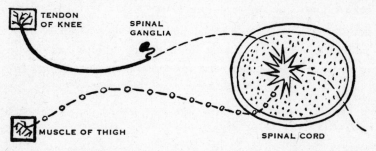

Fig. 63. Diagram of the knee-jerk reflex.

mentioned functions are located in what are considered older parts of the nervous system: the spinal cord, the medulla, the brain stem, and the hypothalamus. All the functions served by the autonomic nervous system are at the subconscious level; they do not depend on our voluntary action. But that they are under some control by the so-called higher centers has been shown repeatedly, and is well exemplified by the psychosomatic manifestations of emotional upsets, such as headaches and peptic ulcers.

The autonomic nervous system although it is controlled by certain areas in the central nervous system, is thought of primarily as existing outside of the brain and spinal cord. All the internal organs contain in their walls the groups of nerve cells called ganglia. These ganglia are in turn connected with others located in various parts of the body such as the regions near the heart, below the diaphragm (the well-known solar plexus), and the pelvis. Then these large groups of ganglia connect, in turn, with chains of ganglia which lie on either side of the vertebral column; and the ganglionic chains connect with the spinal cord. Certain of the cranial nerves—those of the brain—also connect with this network of ganglia.

It is convenient to further divide the autonomic nervous system into two groups, the sympathetic and parasympathetic ganglia and nerves. The thoracolumbar chain along the vertebral column in chest and abdomen belongs to the sympathetic group. The parasympathetic nerves travel longer distances and include those from the cranial and pelvic or sacral regions.

These two systems have actions directly opposing each other. For example, stimulation of the sympathetic system makes the heart beat faster, while the parasympathetic nerve to the heart slows the beat. Parasympathetic nerves ending in the intestine increase peristalsis and secretion when stimulated, while the sympathetic nerves inhibit both movement of the intestine and secretion from its glands.

The other functional subdivision of the nervous system, the somatic nervous system, is concerned with the relation of the body to the outside world.

The Central Nervous System. This consists of the brain and the spinal cord (Pl. XX). They are enclosed in a series of three membranes—the meninges—two very delicate ones, the pia mater and the pia arachnoid, and a third much tougher fibrous mantle, the dura mater. In addition, of course, the brain is enclosed in the bony cranial cavity, and the spinal cord lies protected by a bony canal formed by the vertebral bodies and their dorsal arches. The brain and spinal cord are surrounded by a fluid called the cerebrospinal fluid. This fluid is contained in the hollows of the brain—the ventricles —and it also surrounds the brain and cord in a space between the pia mater and the pia arachnoid called the subarachnoid space. The cerebrospinal fluid, in addition to acting as a cushion to protect the brain and cord, serves the metabolism of the brain in the same way that lymph and tissue fluid serve other tissues in the body. The fluid is made up of the same components as the blood, except that it contains no blood cells and the proportions of the various constituents differ considerably from those in blood. Many diseases of the central nervous system are reflected by changes in the composition of the cerebrospinal fluid, and its examination is of the ut- most importance in almost all such diseases. It is obtained by a lumbar puncture—the puncturing of the subarachnoid space in the lumbar region.

The fact that the brain and spinal cord are surrounded by nonyielding bony envelopes is of tremendous importance in understanding some of the symptoms in diseases of the nervous system, such as tumors.

The spinal cord (Fig. 64) has the appearance of a some- what flattened cylinder about the thickness of one's little finger. It extends from the base of the skull to approximately the lower back. In cross section a central, butterfly-shaped, gray zone can easily be distinguished, surrounded by so- called white matter. The gray zone contains the neurons, while the white matter is formed by the bundles of myelin- covered axons called tracts. Different zones have been recog- nized in the central gray matter of the spinal cord. The an- terior, or ventral, portion contains the neurons from which the motor nerves originate. The posterior, or dorsal, portion contains the associative and sensory neurons. The white matter has also been divided into several tracts fairly easy to recog- nize. There are of course two main types of tracts: those

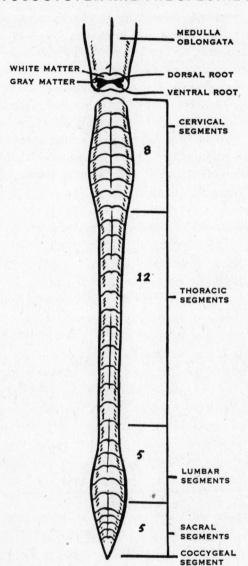

Fig. 64. Length and cross section of the spinal cord.

ascending from the spinal cord to the brain, and called sensory tracts; and those descending from various parts of the brain to the spinal cord, and called motor tracts.

At fairly regular intervals, pairs of "nerves" are seen to leave the spinal cord. These are known as the spinal nerve roots (Fig. 65). There are thirty-one such pairs. Each area of the spinal cord from which a pair originates is known as a spinal segment. This segmental arrangement corresponds to a similar arrangement of the muscles and of the skin, and is of great importance in the clinical examination of the nervous system. We shall return to the spinal roots later, in the discussion of the peripheral nervous system.

The spinal cord has two main functions. First, it serves as a main trunk for conducting and relaying impulses to and from the brain. It is really the most important way station between the limbs and organs and the brain. By way of its sensory tracts go the sensory impulses coming from the skin; and from the brain by way of the cord's motor tracts go impulses that set the neurons in the anterior part of the gray matter into action, so that they send motor impulses to the limbs by way of the spinal roots and thence the motor nerves. The cord's second great function is as one of the most important of the reflex centers. When your hand touches a hot object or when the doctor taps your leg below the kneecap, the sensory impulse, arriving in your spinal cord, activates a group of motor neurons in the same spinal cord segment with an almost immediate response: your hand is withdrawn, your leg swings (Fig. 63). Such action needs no evaluation by the higher brain centers. It is an unthinking, or reflex, action. Of course, such reflex actions *can* be modified by the brain by way of its motor tracts: you *can* keep your hand on the hot stove and you *can* prevent your leg from swinging, but the first, unreasoned, action is the reflex response.

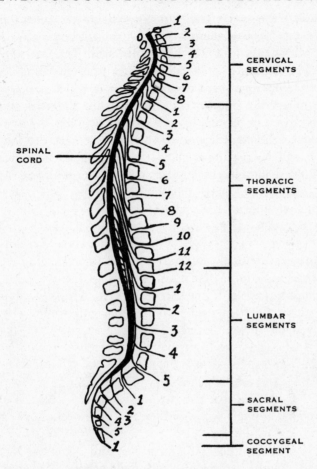

Fig. 65. Spinal nerves (side view).

The sensory tracts of the spinal cord deserve a little more elaboration. They consist of axons sheathed in myelin. The tracts located in the posterior part of the white matter of the spinal cord have their cell bodies located *outside* of the spinal cord; the bodies form a series of ganglia which lie alongside the cord. They are located on the dorsal spinal nerve root. These neurons send their axons as far as three feet, all the way up to the base of the skull. The tracts formed by these axons are concerned with the transmission of special types of sensation, such as position sense, which is concerned with telling the brain in what position the different parts of the body are in relation to each other and to the environment. Other sensations transmitted by way of these tracts are touch and deep pain, such as the pain of a bone bruise or a sprained muscle. In another part of the white matter of the spinal cord, more anterior and to the side, there are tracts that transmit pain and sensations of heat and cold as well as touch.

These sensory impulses, although they travel by different pathways, eventually all end in a certain part of the brain which is called the thalamus. It is from the thalamus that the impulses travel to the cerebral cortex, where the different sensations are then evaluated and recognized for what we know them to be. In other words, we really feel—that is, appreciate—sensations only with our cerebral cortex.

Above the spinal cord is the medulla (Pl. XX and Fig. 66), a part of the brain which is very old, speaking in evolutionary terms. It is there that the two most important centers of the autonomic nervous system are located: the respiratory center, which is concerned with breathing; and the cardiovascular center, which regulates the heartbeat and the entire vascular system. These two centers exert their action by way of one of the cranial nerves, the tenth, or vagus, nerve, which actually belongs to the autonomic nervous system. Several other cranial nerves originate in the medulla. The cranial nerves will be discussed later.

Beyond the medulla is the pons (Pl. XX and Fig. 66). As the name implies, it is a bridge which contains a large number of tracts that connect not only with the medulla and the

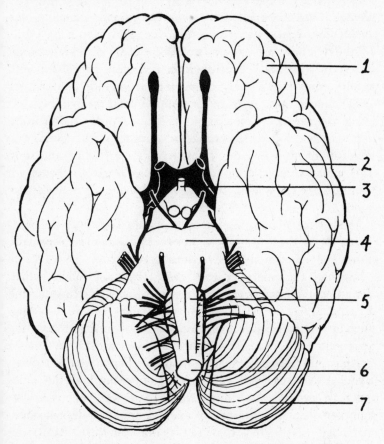

Fig. 66. Undersurface of the brain. (Cranial nerves, black.) 1. Frontal lobe. 2. Temporal lobe. 3. Stalk of pituitary gland. 4. Pons. 5. Medulla. 6. Spinal cord. 7. Cerebellum.

spinal cord, but also with another part of the brain called the cerebellum.

The cerebellum, a name which, literally translated, means the small brain, is situated dorsal to, or astride, the pons and medulla. As the great center for co-ordinating motion, the cerebellum enables us to perform fine movements smoothly. Without it our movements would be coarse, awkward, and jerky. In addition, the cerebellum is greatly concerned with equilibrium. It is closely connected with groups of neurons called nuclei, located in the medulla, which receive impulses from the vestibular mechanism of the ear and enable us to tell whether we are standing, or turning, or bending. The cerebellum receives many tracts from the cerebrum and from the spinal cord, and in turn sends out tracts to the entire central nervous system. It is the great regulator of voluntary motion.

Above the pons is a part of the brain known as the midbrain. It is the area where more cranial nerves, especially those concerned with eye movement, originate.

Beyond the midbrain is a great group of nuclei which form a part of the brain that includes such structures as the basal ganglia, another group of cells concerned with regulation of voluntary movement and closely connected with the cerebellum; the thalamus, which is, so to speak, the sensory sorting and reception center; and the hypothalamic nuclei, which are concerned with the higher control of the autonomic nervous system and are in some way involved with hunger, sleep, and the bodily manifestations of the emotions. Attached to the hypothalamus is the pituitary gland, the so-called master gland of the endocrine system.

The rest of the brain, its greatest part by bulk, consists of the two cerebral hemispheres (Fig. 67). These overlie all the other aforementioned parts of the brain, with the exception of the cerebellum, which is located below them.

The surface of the cerebrum is superficially smooth, but is marked by deep furrows, the sulci, with resulting convolutions known as gyri. Furrows and convolutions have much the same pattern in all human brains, but vary in character

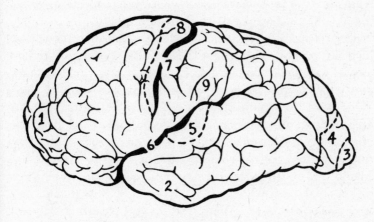

Fig. 67. The cerebrum (side view). 1. Frontal lobe. 2. Temporal lobe (hearing). 3. Visual receptive center. 4. Occipital lobe (vision). 5. Auditory receptive center. 6. Lateral fissure. 7. Central fissure. 8. Motor projection center. 9. Parietal lobe (senses of pain, touch, position, temperature).

in different individuals. In senility there is a tendency for the gyri to shrink and the sulci to widen.

The cerebral hemispheres consist, as do all other parts of the central nervous system, of white and gray matter. The latter, which is near the surface of the brain and contains the neurons, is called the cerebral cortex. It is the great development of the cerebral cortex that differentiates man from the lower vertebrates.

The cerebral hemispheres are divided into lobes. These are named according to the area of the skull which overlies them. It has been found that certain functions can be ascribed to particular lobes of the cerebral hemispheres. Of course, it must be understood that the important parts of the hemispheres are the areas of cerebral cortex or gray matter overlying them. The bulk of the hemispheres consists of white matter—the tracts going to and from the cortex.

The frontal lobe, which is better developed in man than in other primates, is believed to be the site of the highest mental functions, such as judgment, reasoning, and planning, as well as appreciation of certain sensations such as pain. What have been rather loosely called the emotions probably also originate in some part of the frontal lobe, and these are of course related in some way to the appreciation and evaluation of certain outside stimuli which we call sensations. The frontal lobe receives many tracts from, and sends many tracts to, the thalamus, which, as we have seen, is the great sensory reception center. When the tracts between the frontal lobe and the thalamus are severed, as they are in a frontal lobotomy, the patient, although he or she still receives sensory impulses, is now unable to appreciate them. Thus pain is felt as a definite and recognizable stimulus, but the sensation is no longer appreciated as an unpleasant or "painful" one. At the same time, destroying the connections of the frontal lobes with the rest of the brain impairs the functions ascribed to the frontal lobe, such as judgment and planning. No part of the cerebral hemispheres can function unless it remains a part of the complex mechanism that is the brain. The functions that are ascribed to a certain part of the cortex are probably not specifically located in that particular part but, when that area of the cortex is functioning as part of the entire mechanism, these functions are best regulated and refined by such an area.

The posterior part of the frontal lobe is concerned with voluntary movement. A certain area of the cortex in that part of the frontal lobe contains neurons in which the impulse for voluntary movement originates. From these neurons—and modified by impulses that act upon them and that have come from other parts of the cortex, from the basal ganglia, and from the cerebellum—the axons descend all the way down to the spinal cord to terminate close to the dendrites of the neurons in the anterior part of the gray matter of the cord. In their descent the tracts formed by these axons cross over to the other side. As a matter of fact, all the sensory tracts previously described have crossed to the other side. It is therefore easy to understand why it is that the left hemisphere of the brain governs the right side of the body while the right hemisphere governs the left side of the body.

The parietal lobes are concerned mainly with what can be called nonspecialized sensation, as opposed to sensory impulses conveyed to the brain by the organs of the special senses of sight and hearing. From the thalamus great groups of tracts end in the parietal lobes to which they carry impulses that were first relayed in the spinal cord. Touch, position sense, some components of pain, and temperature sensations are all relayed to the parietal lobes.

The occipital lobes are almost exclusively concerned with the reception and evaluation of visual impulses—that is, the sense of sight.

The temporal lobes are centers for the reception of impulses originating in the ear; that is, they are the centers for audition.

The parietal, occipital, and temporal lobes, or actually certain areas of the cortex that cover these lobes, receive the "unevaluated" sensory perceptions. Large areas of the cortex comprising the posterior part of the parietal and temporal lobes as well as the anterior part of the occipital lobes are what are called association areas. It is in these areas of the cortex that the different sensations are interpreted, evaluated, and correlated with other sensory impulses received either at the same time or at some time in the past. There probably reside the different types of memory: the visual, the auditory, and the tactile. And in the association areas of the cortex are localized the different functions that really make man a superior animal. It is by combination of these different types of memory that we are able to speak and read and write, to calculate, to tell our right from our left, to point to different parts of our body, to remember directions, to find our way, to recognize songs and play musical instruments, to recognize objects by touch as well as by sight, and to tell colors from each other.

All these very specialized functions are restricted to one cerebral hemisphere. In right-handed people, the left hemisphere is the seat of these functions. For that reason the left hemisphere of right-handed people is called the major or dominant hemisphere. The reverse is not entirely true; that is, the right hemisphere is not quite as "dominant" in a left-handed person.

It must be emphasized that regardless of the actual localization of function, all these areas of the cortex are interconnected by vast and complicated networks of axons. No one area can function unless its connections, both to and fro, are intact. Conversely, a specific function can be impaired if the tracts from, as well as to, the area concerned are injured. The brain, functionally, can be compared to a number of batteries connected in series. Take one out and the whole system collapses. Even though certain specific functions can be ascribed to certain specific cortical areas, the brain as a whole governs and regulates all functions.

The Peripheral Nervous System. This consists of the cranial nerves, the spinal roots, and the nerve trunks. There are twelve pairs of cranial nerves (Pl. XXI). These originate in different parts of the brain, but all excepting the first two are found connected with what has been called the axial part of the brain—the brain stem which consists of the medulla, pons, and midbrain (Fig. 66).

The first cranial nerve is called the olfactory nerve, and it is concerned with the sense of smell. It consists of a whole group of small nerves that connect the sensory membrane of the nose to an undersurface extension of the brain called the olfactory bulb. The olfactory system, which is extremely well developed in animals, is almost nonexistent in man. However, its parts in the brain have been found to be of importance in the emotional regulation of autonomic nervous function, and they form what some have called the visceral brain.

The second, or optic, nerve is concerned with vision. It is incorrectly named, as it is really an integral part of the brain. The axons that form this "nerve" go all the way from the retina to the occipital lobe. Each optic nerve serves half of the retina of each eye. The axons of the optic nerve also cross, so that what we see to our left, using both eyes, is actually recorded on the right occipital cortex.

The third, or oculomotor, fourth, or trochlear, and sixth, or abducens, nerves innervate the six small muscles that move the eyeball and the muscles of the eyelid. The action of the eyeball and eyelid muscles must be very accurately coordinated in order that useful vision can be maintained. The nuclei of origin of the three pairs of nerves concerned with the ocular movements are all closely connected. They also receive connections with other nuclei in the brain stem that are concerned with the reception of impulses such as hearing and touch, as well as other functions such as equilibrium. The size of the pupil is also governed by the third nerve. Many reflex actions are mediated by way of these nerves and their nuclei.

The fifth, or trigeminal, nerve is a mixed nerve; that is, it has both motor and sensory components. The motor component innervates the muscles with which we chew, while the sensory component brings in sensation from the entire face.

The seventh, or facial, nerve is also mixed. Its sensory

component carries taste from the anterior two thirds of the tongue. Its motor part innervates the muscles of the face that make us smile, wrinkle our foreheads, wiggle our ears, and open our mouths.

The eighth nerve actually consists of two distinct and separate nerves. The cochlear division is the nerve of hearing. The vestibular division carries impulses that originate in the vestibular mechanism of the ear, and is concerned with equilibrium.

The ninth, or glossopharyngeal, nerve carries taste from the posterior third of the tongue, carries sensation from the mouth, and helps in the act of swallowing and in the production of saliva.

The tenth, or vagus, nerve has many functions. It is the great pathway for the autonomic nervous system's regulation of the cardiovascular, respiratory, and gastrointestinal systems. In addition it also innervates the vocal cords, and is concerned with some phases of swallowing.

The eleventh, or spinal accessory, nerve is purely motor and innervates the muscles that allow us to turn our heads and shrug our shoulders.

The twelfth, or hypoglossal, nerve innervates the muscles of the tongue.

Each spinal-cord segment also gives rise to a pair of spinal nerve roots (Fig. 65), one on the right and one on the left. Each spinal nerve root is actually the result of the fusion of a motor root which originates in the ventral surface of the cord and a sensory root which is attached to the dorsal surface of the cord. Fastened to the dorsal root is the sensory ganglion, which is composed of the bodies of the sensory nerves that carry sensation from the skin and organs by way of the sensory tracts of the cord to the brain. The ventral, or motor, root contains the axons of the neurons in the ventral gray matter of the cord. The motor and sensory roots thus fuse to form a mixed nerve. Shortly after this fusion a branch is sent to and received from the corresponding autonomic-nervous-system ganglion that lies outside of the spinal canal but alongside the vertebral column and is part of the main ganglionic chain. It is by way of these branches that the autonomic nervous system is connected with the spinal cord and the brain.

In the areas of the chest and the abdomen the mixed nerves innervate areas of muscle and skin that can easily be seen to correspond to the segments from which the nerves originate in the spinal cord. Such segmental areas of skin are known as dermatomes.

The innervation of the extremities is somewhat more complicated, although the basic arrangement of a spinal-cord segment that sends a nerve to or receives a nerve from a corresponding dermatome is maintained. The segmental arrangement of muscle is much more difficult to detect, however, as the original embryological muscle groups, the myotomes which correspond to the cord segments, were fused in order for the muscle groups to achieve usable mechanical function.

Shortly after leaving the spinal cord the nerves that serve the arms and the legs are grouped into networks of mixed (sensory and motor) nerves called plexuses. The brachial plexus (Pl. XXIII) is made up of nerves originating in the fourth, fifth, sixth, seventh, and eighth cervical and first thoracic segments, while the lumbosacral plexus which innervates the leg is made up of spinal nerve roots originating in all the lumbar and sacral nerve segments.

After fusing into plexuses the nerves again divide, but this time the segmental arrangement has been given up in favor of a more functional one. Nerves are formed which may have components arising in different spinal-cord segments. From the brachial plexus the musculocutaneous nerve, which innervates the biceps, gets axons from the fourth, fifth, and sixth segments; while the radial nerve, which innervates the extensors of the arm and fingers, gets axons from all but the first segments that participate in the formation of the brachial plexus. The same holds true for the nerves such as the sciatic or femoral that issue from the lumbosacral plexus (Pl. XXII).

The motor nerves of the peripheral nervous system all end in a specialized structure which is called the motor-end plate and which is intimately associated with the striated muscle fibers that make up the muscle.

Sensation coming from the skin, bones, joints, and tendons is transmitted by way of the same nerves that carry motor axons, but now this sensation is carried by very long dendrites which belong to the neuron located in the dorsal root ganglion.

Different types of sensations are recorded by different types of specialized structures just below the skin, in the tendons, or in the membrane surrounding bone. Pain is mediated by simple, fine, naked nerve endings. Touch is received by tangled networks of small nerve fibers called Meissner's corpuscles, while deep pressure is believed to activate an impulse in an onionlike structure called a Pacinian body. Cold is believed to be mediated by a spherical arrangement of nerves called Krause's end-bulb, and heat is transmitted by still other structures called corpuscles of Ruffini. The segmental nature of innervation is maintained; and, although the peripheral nerve contains sensory fibers going to several cord segments, all the sensory impulses from the specific area of skin called the dermatome end up in the corresponding spinal-cord segment. It is thus possible, by pricking with a pin to delineate sensory impairment, to determine at what level an injury of the spinal cord is. By knowing which muscles are innervated by what peripheral nerves, and by knowing what spinal segments contribute to the make-up of each specific motor nerve, it is also possible to place an injury at the correct spinal-cord level.

164

THE SPECIAL SENSES

Sight. Much of our sensory perception follows actual contact of our nerve endings with the stimulant, and therefore makes us aware only of our immediate external or internal environment. Sight allows us to receive impressions from greater distances and helps give us the concept of ourselves in space and in relation to other objects. It is difficult for seeing individuals to imagine what mental images can be formed by someone blind from birth.

The eye is protected from common injury by its position deep in a bony socket. The eyeball lies in a padding of fat which cushions it against a blow to the head. The exposed surface is amply covered by a readily movable shade, the eyelid, which, when possible danger approaches, closes by reflex action although it is also under voluntary control. The eyelashes provide additional means of preventing injurious particles from having contact with the eye.

We have only to recall that we have evolved from aquatic animals to realize that the eye was expected to function in water, not in air—and it still does so in man. A constant flow of salty fluid which is secreted by the lacrimal glands bathes the exposed surface of the eye and is drained into the nose through the lacrimal duct (Fig. 68). We call this fluid tears when excessive formation al-

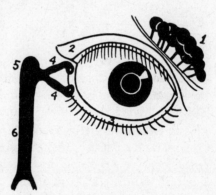

Fig. 68. The lacrimal gland and ducts of the eye. 1. Lacrimal gland. 2. Upper lid. 3. Lower lid. 4. Lacrimal ducts. 5. Lacrimal sac. 6. Nasal duct.

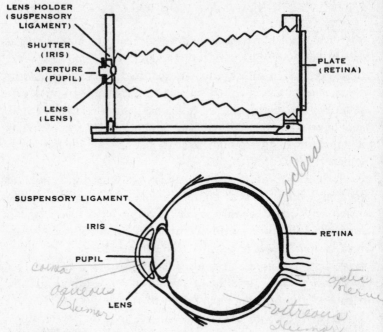

Fig. 69. The human eye and a camera, in cross sections.

lows it to spill over the lower lid. Besides salt (sodium chloride) and a little mucus and albumin, the lacrimal fluid contains a bacteria-destroying substance known as lysozyme. This is a highly effective deterrent to infection by the organisms to which we are constantly exposed.

As was previously stated, the eye is capable of limited rotation because of six balanced ocular muscles innervated by the third, fourth, and sixth cranial nerves. It is most important that the two eyes move in absolute unison if we are to avoid seeing double. To enable us to focus both eyes on a fine point, co-ordination of the ocular muscles is highly developed.

The eyes are seldom, if ever, perfectly still. We are usually unsuccessful in feigning sleep if our eyes are watched, because it is too difficult for us to prevent their moving more continually than they do in sleep.

The eye is a spherical structure of which only a small part of the surface is visible. It is a highly complex optical instrument after which the camera, a far simpler structure, is patterned (Fig. 69). The interior of the eyeball is roughly divided into a small front section which contains thin, watery, clear fluid (aqueous fluid), and a large main section which contains a gelatinous material (vitreous fluid). These fluids circulate slowly and have interchange with the blood stream to a limited extent. One striking difference from the blood stream, however, is that the fluids of the eye do not contain antibodies. Experimental biologists have taken advantage of this feature to grow foreign tissues from other species in the front chamber of the eyes of guinea pigs or rabbits, where the foreign tissues' response to specific drugs can be observed directly.

In the eye is found the only truly transparent tissue of the adult human body, and this transparency is of the greatest importance. The cornea (Fig. 70) is the slightly curved, clear front window through which all light which the eye en-

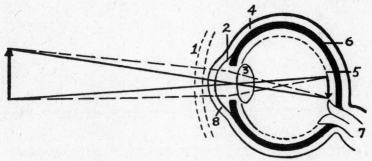

Fig. 70. Inverted image of an arrow as it appears on the retina of the eye. 1. Eyelid. 2. Iris. 3. Lens. 4. Sclera. 5. Retina. 6. Chorioid. 7. Optic nerve. 8. Cornea.

counters must pass. Actually the cornea is continuous with the skin and, like the skin, is composed of layered epithelium and connective tissue. Unlike the skin, however, it has no pigment at all, and its connective tissue contains no blood vessels. When the cornea is injured it can repair itself as readily as the skin does, but blood vessels are likely to grow into it and spoil its capacity for transmitting light. The condition of the rest of the eye may be excellent, but if the cornea is clouded we cannot see.

Fortunately the cornea has a capacity for long life beyond that of the rest of the body. In fact, we do not know the limits of that capacity. That is why it is possible to remove the cornea from an individual who has just died and transplant it in another person to replace a cornea that has become scarred or clouded. Such an operation is used extensively today to restore sight to those with poor corneas.

A short distance behind the cornea, and separated from it by aqueous fluid, lies the lens, which is partly covered by the colored diaphragm called the iris (Fig. 69). The actions of lens and diaphragm are co-ordinated to allow us to receive sharp images, or to focus on near objects as well as far.

The lens is a biconvex disc. That is, it is thick in the middle and curves to a thin sheet at the edges. Like a biconvex glass lens it receives parallel rays of light and converges them to a focal point, in this instance the back of the eye where visual impressions are received (Fig. 70). The lens is suspended by ligaments which are stretched or relaxed by the action of tiny muscles at the sides. Contraction and relaxation of these muscles change the shape of the lens and hence change the degree of refraction, or bending, of the light rays.

Like the cornea, the lens is also composed of bloodless, transparent, colorless tissue. A cloudy change called a cataract may appear in the lens and obscure vision to a marked degree. This condition occurs more frequently in elderly people than in others. But a lens can be removed, and glasses for near vision can compensate for its loss.

The size of the aperture through which light reaches the lens is controlled by the iris. This is the pigmented ring which we can readily see in another's eyes. The pupil is the hole which appears as a black spot in the center of the iris. Its size is changed by reflex reaction to light or on accommodation to near and far objects.

In order to bring near objects sharply in focus the iris and lens change together. The lens rounds up, becomes more convex due to relaxation of the muscles, and the sphincter muscle of the iris contracts and closes the aperture sufficiently for better definition. These changes occur by reflex action. With age we are less able to accommodate for near vision and commonly require reading glasses.

The retina, the inner lining of the bulb of the eye, contains the sensory end organs of sight. In a camera photographic film is its crude counterpart. But in the retina the change which forms the image is rapidly reversible and the same cells quickly form new images. If a person fixes his eyes on a scene partly in bright light, the dark and light contours can still be seen when his lids are closed, but they soon fade.

The retina contains highly specialized cells, called rods and cones, found nowhere else in the body. They are the receptors. The rods give awareness of brightness, and the cones give color to the image. In the back of the retina the rods and cones connect by synapse with ganglion cells whose axons extend around the eye and join to form the optic nerve. Through the optic nerve impulses are conducted to the brain.

The process by which light is transformed into nervous impulses which convey a picture is subject only to theorizing. One part is clear. A red pigment called visual purple is present in the rods. Light, acting upon this pigment, decomposes it, and the products of decomposition stimulate the nerves. The more pigment we have, the better we can adapt to vision in the dark. Visual purple is rapidly resynthesized, else we could not continue to see. It is possible, however, to injure the rods by exposing them to too bright a light, as we do when we look directly at the sun. As a result of excessive exposure of this kind there will be permanent spots of poor vision.

Color vision is best in the center of the retina, the spot which receives the image of an object at which we are looking directly. At the periphery of the retina the rods are more numerous and night vision is best.

The mechanism of color vision is not clearly understood. It has been postulated that different cones contain different photosensitive substances which are stimulated by specific colors, and that these stimuli are conducted along certain axons to certain nerve cells in the brain. Complete "color blindness" rarely exists. But there are different degrees and many congenital variations in the ability to recognize colors. These variations are presumably due to differences in the content of the cones.

The shape of the eye—whether it is perfectly rounded, or elongated, or compressed from front to back—alters our ability to focus light sharply on the retina. It also determines whether we are nearsighted or farsighted. Irregularities of the shape of the eye produce distortions called astigmatism. We can do much to correct these distortions by wearing glasses with the proper lenses.

The main blood vessels of the eye enter it through the optic nerve and branch through the retina. These vessels can be seen when the eyes are examined with an ophthalmoscope, which provides a good view of the state of the small arteries of the eye. Arteriosclerosis, high blood pressure, diabetes, kidney failure, and other diseases may produce changes in the arteries or the surrounding retinal tissue which are visible to the examiner.

The optic or second cranial nerve head leads off from the back of the eyeballs, but a little to one side of the center (Fig. 70). Where it goes through the retina there is a very small blind spot where sensory nerves are lacking. The optic nerves from the two eyes join inside the cranial cavity. Here the axons from the inner, or nasal, half of each retina cross to the other side.

The axons continue as the optic tracts to the midbrain. Optic reflexes make the circuit this far. For recognition and understanding of the visual images, cortical tracts continue to the inner aspect of the occipital lobes. We see, then, in the hindmost part of the brain.

Binocular or stereoscopic vision depends upon the very slightly different images received by each eye because of its position in relation to the object (Fig. 71). The brain combines the two pictures into one with depth. An ordinary camera takes a single picture which appears flat. A stereoscopic camera makes use of the same principle as that of the eye. Light which reaches the film through two separated lenses produces in the picture contours which our brains interpret as a third dimension.

Audition. Hearing, like sight, allows us to receive sensory impulses which originate at a distance. While our well-being is less dependent upon acute hearing than it is upon sight, hearing is an important means of understanding and of protection. People with poor hearing often keep a watchdog, since their own alerting mechanism is faulty.

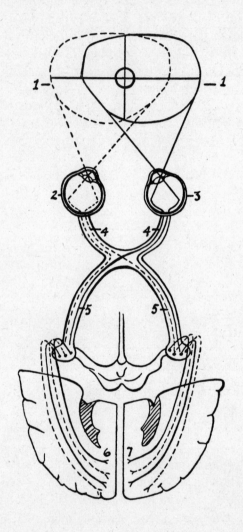

Fig. 71. Optic pathway—stereoscopic vision. 1. Image. 2. Left eye. 3. Right eye. 4. Optic nerves. 5. Optic tracts. 6. Left occipital lobe. 7. Right occipital lobe.

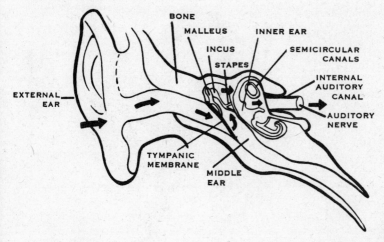

Fig. 72. Cross section of the ear, showing route which sound travels.

The auditory mechanism (Fig. 72) includes an external ear which catches the sound waves; an air-filled middle ear which transmits the waves; and a fluid-filled inner ear which has the end organs of hearing, the receptors. From these the auditory nerve and its pathways connect with the hearing centers of the brain.

The auricle, or external ear (the part of the ear we see), is not essential for hearing. We can hear without it and could substitute the cupped hand for the cartilaginous structure we possess. Its canal is lubricated by a secretion like the sebaceous secretion from the skin. As this congeals, it forms the wax or cerumen which can interfere with hearing if it is allowed to accumulate.

At the end of the canal a slightly funnel-shaped sheet, the eardrum, or tympanic membrane, closes the channel completely. Sound waves which impinge on this membrane set up the vibrations that are eventually recognized in the brain

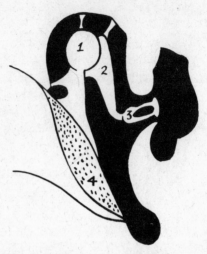

Fig. 73. The middle ear. 1. Malleus (hammer). 2. Incus (anvil). 3. Stapes (stirrup). 4. Tympanic membrane.

as sound. If the membrane becomes thickened by repeated infection or if it is lost, hearing is greatly impaired.

In the middle ear (Fig. 73), directly behind the tympanic membrane, three minute bones in the form of a chain transmit vibrations to the membrane of the oval window between the middle and inner chambers. The three bones are named for their shapes. The malleus (hammer) attaches to the tympanic membrane by its handle. Its head joins the uncus (anvil), which attaches to the stapes (stirrup). The foot of the stapes lies against the membrane of the oval window. If the ligaments which connect these tiny bones harden so that vibration is impaired, partial deafness develops. Some vibration can be transmitted through the air.

Air in the middle ear is always being absorbed, but this chamber is connected with the pharynx by the Eustachian tube. As we swallow or cough or sneeze we force air into the tube to replenish the air in the ear and equalize pressure on either side of the tympanic membrane. At times, as when we have a cold, mucus plugs the openings in the pharynx. This makes us uncomfortable and partly deafened by the reduced pressure in the middle ear and the bulging inward of the membrane. As we rise in an airplane, on the other hand, the membrane is forced outward until we swallow and admit the air with lower pressure at the higher altitude.

Infections in the middle ear sometimes follow throat infections, and pus may replace the air. A sharp slit in the eardrum permits the escape of pus, and the membrane can heal. Repeated infections, however, may leave poorly vibrating membrane and bones.

The inner ear (Fig. 74) is filled with fluid. Vibrations of the membrane which stretches over the oval window are

Fig. 74. The inner ear. 1. Cochlea. 2. Posterior semicircular canal. 3. Superior semicircular canal. 4. Lateral semicircular canal. 5. Malleus (hammer). 6. Incus (anvil). 7. Stapes (stirrup). 8. Tympanic membrane. 9. Vestibular nerve. 10. Facial nerve. 11. Cochlear nerve.

transmitted across the fluid to the end organ of the nervous component of hearing, the cochlea. This is a fluid-filled tube a little over an inch long, coiled somewhat like the shell of a snail. In the cochlea there are cells with hairy projections which pick up the waves from the fluid. The impulse is transmitted by synapse to the ganglia of the eighth cranial, or auditory, nerve, which sends axons toward the brain.

An entirely distinct pathway for transmission of sound to the auditory nerve is by bone conduction. This is a relatively inefficient means for the spread of sound waves. However, a tuning fork held against the bone behind the ear is readily "heard" even though there may be middle-ear deafness. This is the basic principle for the operation of the hearing aids used by many deaf persons.

The nerve pathway to the brain is a relatively short one. However, the hearing pathway through the medulla and midbrain is more complex than are the optic tracts and has many nuclei which are probably involved in reflex actions. Some axons cross and some remain on the same side to reach the hearing centers in the temporal lobes, the part of the brain near the ears.

Equilibrium. Without balance we cannot maintain an erect posture. Our sense of balance is dependent upon multiple sensations from skin, muscles, eyes, and from a portion of the inner ear called the semicircular canals (Fig. 74). The most vital contributors to our equilibrium are these structures in the inner ear. Their three canals are curved tubes set at right angles in three planes, like the bottom and two adjacent sides of a box. Each has a dilated end furnished with nerve receptors and hair-tipped cells. The canals are partly filled with fluid which moves with each movement of the head. As the head rotates, displaced fluid presses more on some hairy cells than on others and we know from experience what position our head has assumed. But if we whirl around rapidly, the splashing which continues after we stop leaves us confused and dizzy. We must wait until the fluid calms down before we know where we are in relation to our surroundings.

Two other small structures in this region, the utricle and the saccule, help to maintain balance. These structures also have a patch of hairy cells, but the hairs in this instance are in contact with a gelatinous substance which contains little calcium crystals. As the shifting crystals change position with relation to gravity, they stimulate the hairy cells to tell us the position of the head in space.

Taste. It is difficult to separate the psychological and the anatomical aspects of our taste sensibilities, since there is involved such a very large emotional component based on our experiences. Infants have taste buds just as adults do. In fact they have more, since, with age, the number of receptors gradually diminishes from several hundred to about seventy or eighty in elderly people. Yet, because the infant has not formed an opinion and is most concerned with satisfying hunger and thirst, he is not disturbed by flavors which would be unpleasant to many adults. Many a mother is surprised at the ease with which an infant or child continues to swallow a bitter liquid vitamin mixture the odor of which is repugnant to her. It is for this reason that pediatricians urge parents not to express dislikes for foods in front of children. The appreciation of flavors and the ideas concerning them are largely a matter of training, and they depend upon all the circumstances associated with the taking of the food.

The state of the body as a whole also enters into our desire or lack of desire for a particular substance which is identified by its taste. After animals have been made deficient in certain substances such as calcium or magnesium, they will then give preference to the water or food which contains these missing substances. If their ability to taste is destroyed they show no preference. More limited studies have been carried out which indicate that children eventually respond in the same manner when they are given free choice of many foods.

A further confusion arises from the close association of taste and smell, the gustatory and olfactory senses. Much that we regard as having a distinctive flavor we have really appreciated as an odor. Food tastes flat when we have a cold that obstructs the nose. For this reason the neural tracts and cerebral centers of the two senses were once thought to be closely related. However, it is recognized now that taste sensation is in the location of pathways more closely associated with other sensory and motor tracts to and from the tongue and throat.

We are reminded of our aquatic ancestry whenever we see that structures function only in a fluid medium. This is true of taste mechanisms as well as those of sight and hearing. Unless material

Fig. 75. A single taste bud.

is in solution it does not affect the taste sensory endings. In fish these are located in many parts of the skin and gills as well as in the mouth. In man they are essentially limited to tongue and pharynx, with the tongue containing the most active ones. A moderate amount of taste sensation is appreciated about the epiglottis and the tonsillar region.

A taste bud (Fig. 75) is made up of cylindrical nerve cells grouped somewhat in the shape of a narrow-necked flask. The cells extending through the neck to the surface have tiny hairs which come in contact with the flavored liquid. All the taste buds look very much alike, but it seems likely that individual receptors are affected by different types of taste. We recognize four catagories: bitter, sour, sweet, and salt. That these are associated with particular taste buds is suggested by the fact that by using specific chemicals we can block the effect of one or more types of taste and leave the others intact. In reality these groups of flavors are so mixed that we do not separate them in our minds unless one predominates. We do not recognize salt unless the food is too salty, or unless we can appreciate salt's absence.

The specificity of taste buds would also explain the observation that different types of flavor are best appreciated in different regions of the tongue (Fig. 76). The tip can receive all flavors, but it is most sensitive to salt and sweet. The back of the tongue recognizes bitter. On the sides, sour and salt are effective. The top of the tongue is the least sensitive, and one can hold bitter medicine there for some time before recognition comes with swallowing.

The neural pathway for taste is simple compared with those for sight and hearing. The axons from the back third of the tongue travel up the ninth cranial, or glossopharyngeal, nerve. Those from the forward two thirds join the seventh cranial, or facial, nerve. They form numerous connections

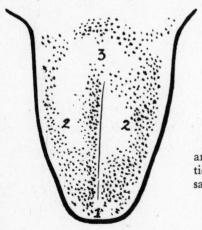

Fig. 76. Tongue, showing areas of different taste sensations. 1. Salt, sweet. 2. Sour, salt. 3. Bitter.

after they enter the medulla; pass through the midbrain; and seem to terminate in the lower part of the parietal lobe of the cortex, near the centers for receiving other types of sensation from the mouth. Our memory for tastes and our highly developed association of a flavor with an event in our past is attributed to the manifold 'associative tracts in the brain.

Not everyone is equally capable of developing appreciation of all tastes. Despite experience, a small percentage of individuals lack some part of the taste mechanism and have degrees of taste failure comparable to those of color blindness. Perhaps particular receptors are congenitally underdeveloped.

Smell. The olfactory sense is one of the least vital to man, but it adds much to his awareness of his surroundings. As air is drawn into the nose it passes directly back through the lower passages and reaches the upper chamber only secondarily, after it has been filtered and partly warmed. Here it encounters the special nerve endings (Fig. 77), the receptors for the sense of smell, which lie only in the region at about the level of the eyes. In structure and behavior they resemble the taste buds in the tongue. Minute hairs on the surface come in contact with the odor, which must be dissolved in the nasal secretions to be appreciated. This is another example of a body mechanism which functions only when moisture is present.

The receptors send axons back through the bone of the skull to a bulbous end of the first cranial nerve, the olfactory nerve. Hence axons enter the midbrain and after many ramifications reach the olfactory center in the temporal lobe.

We ourselves are aware of the many associations that we make between experience and the appreciation of odors. Such memories endure many years. However, exact testing of the sense of smell and its cerebral pathways is difficult and much remains to be learned about it. Exactly how the odor affects

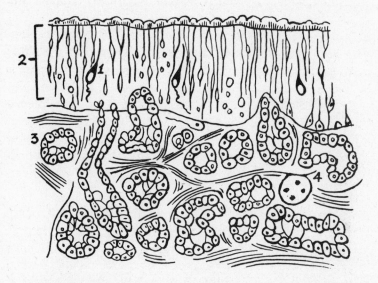

Fig. 77. Olfactory mucous membrane of the nose. 1. Olfactory nerve cell. 2. Epithelium. 3. Secretory glands. 4. Nerve bundles.

the cell, whether by chemical or physical change, is not known. We do know, however, that the nose can become "fatigued" and that we no longer appreciate one odor to which we have been exposed for some time, although that same "fatigued" nasal tissue is immediately sensitive to another odor of a different character.

Bone. The framework of the body is composed of 206 bones of various sizes and shapes, which help give firm but flexible support to the soft tissues and organs. Each individual bone is a rigid structure, but because our bones are jointed, limited movement of a part of the body is possible. The character of the joints between the many bones determines the degree and quality of motion which can be performed. Motion is then effected by the muscles.

The bones, and the marrow which most of them contain, are really two unrelated systems. The marrow gives rise to blood cells, as was described in Chapter 3. Its only association with the bone is one of proximity.

All bones have an outer compact layer, the cortex, and an inner latticework of connecting spicules among which the marrow (Fig. 78) is dispersed. The relative amount of the dense cortical bone and of the inner spongy bone varies greatly. Those bones that require strength have the heaviest cortex.

The cortex is covered by a tough fibrous capsule, the periosteum. To this are attached tendons of the muscles and ligaments of the joints.

Despite its appearance of ivorylike solidity, cortical bone

is a living tissue with many vessels. Arteries are numerous in the periosteum and penetrate into the cortical bone as one or more main nutrient vessels. This apparently solid bone tissue is actually permeated by ramifying channels, the Haversian canals, through which the blood vessels can reach all parts of the cortex and enter the central marrow compartment. The veins are also numerous and larger than the arteries, so that the channels in which they lie may be visible in a flat bone like the skull. Nerves follow the nutrient arteries, but are most numerous in the periosteum.

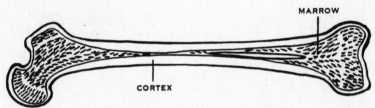

MARROW

CORTEX

Fig. 78. A cross section of bone (femur).

Throughout the outer cortical and the inner spongy bone are small spaces containing the bone cells (Fig. 79). The presence of living cells is just as important to bone as to any other tissue of the body.

Bone is composed of a mucoid-protein ground substance called osteoid (or bonelike), in which mineral salts are deposited. About 95 per cent of the inorganic substance is a complex calcium-phosphate-carbonate compound in a constant state of flux. It is easy to see how one might erroneously regard bone as an inert nonliving structure. We can remove a bone from soft tissues, clean it, and boil it, yet its structure is apparently intact. In the living body, however, bone is quite as dynamic as any other organ. Its salts are being deposited and reabsorbed in a continuous turnover which is

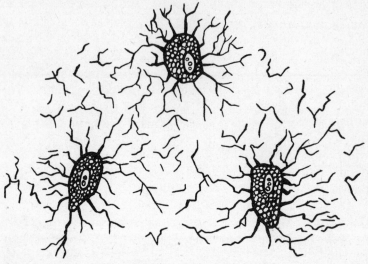

Fig. 79. Bone cells.

readily demonstrated by tracing the pathway of radioactive minerals after injection.

While the chemical composition of the skeleton varies with age, with the character of food, and with the state of activity of the endocrine glands, there are some generalizations about it which prevail throughout life. Most of the phosphorus and over 99 per cent of the calcium of the body are present in the skeleton. About half of the body magnesium and a quarter of the stores of sodium and chloride are to be found in the bone. All are continuously coming and going as part of the body's dynamic equilibrium.

The parathyroid glands are most prominently concerned with the regulation of the calcium-phosphorus equilibrium on which our bones are dependent for strength. These tiny glands need only be overactive and the skeleton may become so soft that the bones can eventually be bent and twisted like the legs of a rag doll. The enlargement of an overactive parathyroid gland is so inconspicuous that often it cannot be felt or seen except by a surgeon who searches for it; its malfunction can only be suspected. An x-ray showing decalcification of the bone or a study of the composition of the blood may be important clues to an abnormal parathyroid condition.

A malfunctioning parathyroid gland probably affects bone indirectly by increasing the excretion of phosphorus in the urine. More phosphorus is then drawn from the bone into the depleted blood, and along with it comes the calcium, which remains at a high level in the blood. Removal of a tiny parathyroid tumor or enlarged gland is followed by restoration of the normal bone composition.

Another factor influencing the amount of calcium salts in the bone is an adequate ingestion of vitamin D or exposure to ultraviolet light so that the skin can manufacture vitamin D. When vitamin D is deficient in a growing child the absorption of calcium and phosphorus from the intestinal tract is poor and the bones become soft with deformities. Rickets, as this unfortunate condition is called, has all but disappeared in many parts of the world, but it still exists where ignorance or poverty prevail.

Despite the continuous interchange of minerals in the bone we do not regard adult bone as growing, since the overall size remains essentially the same. However, that the adult skeleton is capable of rapid bone growth is evidenced by the healing of a fracture. If the fragments are well aligned so that normal stresses and strains are brought to bear on it, regrowth of the bone across the fracture may be so complete as to defy detection of the site of injury.

The Skeleton. The pattern of the skeletal system (Pl. XXIV) consists of a long spinal column made up of a series of specially shaped rings called the vertebrae to which are attached the head, the thoracic cage, and the pelvic bones. The bones of the lower extremities articulate with the latter. Those of the upper extremities extend from the shoulder girdle, which in turn attaches to the thoracic cage.

The various joints of the skeletal system are dissimilar in structure, hence allowing for much variation in the degree and character of the motion they permit. However, they can be conveniently arranged in three classes to designate the pattern of their action. Marked differences in structure account for their limitation or freedom of action.

Those bones which cannot move, the synarthroses, such as the flat bones of the skull, are separated only by fibrous tissue. Those capable of quite limited motion, the amphiarthroses, such as the segments of the spine, are joined by a thick band of fibrous and cartilaginous tissue. In the freely movable diarthroses, which comprise the majority of joints, the bones are actually separated, but are held in close approximation by a fibrous capsule which attaches above and below the contiguous surfaces. The joint space is filled with a mucoid fluid, the synovial fluid, which lubricates the articulating surfaces and facilitates motion. Because this fluid is secreted by the synovial membrane which partly lines the joint space, these joints are referred to as synovial joints. The extremities of bones which form synovial joints are composed of cartilage. This has more resilience than bone, and forms smooth, polished, well-fitted articulating surfaces.

The highly movable synovial joints can be further classified according to the type of motion they permit. This is determined in part by the contours of the articulating surfaces and in part by the attachment of restraining ligaments.

Some joints are limited to motion in one axis. Some bend in one plane, as do the hinge joints of the fingers or the knee (Pl. XXVII); and some move in a pivotlike fashion, as do the joints between the radius and ulna bones of the forearm (Pl. XXV).

Condyloid and saddle joints are essentially similar, in that

all motion except rotation is per-
mitted. They differ somewhat in
shape. The condyloid articulating surfaces are elliptical, as at
the wrist. The saddle joint forms
a deeper concavoconvexity. The
joint between thumb and hand
bone is a good example of a
saddle joint (Pl. XXV).

The shoulder and hip joints
are capable of motion in any
axis. Their articulating surfaces
resemble a ball and socket (Pl.
XXVI), and they are designated
accordingly.

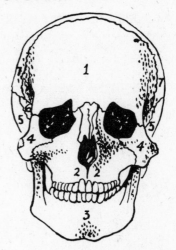

Fig. 80. Bones of the skull
(front). 1. Frontal. 2. Maxilla. 3. Mandible. 4. Zygo-
matic. 5. Temporal. 6.
Sphenoid. 7. Parietal.

Some joint surfaces are almost
flat or are only very slightly
curved, and motion is limited
to a gliding action by ligaments.
Such joints are known as
arthrodia. Examples of arthrodia are the articulating surfaces
of processes which extend from the main segments, or bodies,
of the spine. Although the articulating processes have synovial joints, which ordinarily move with greater freedom,
strong back muscles and ligaments as well as the fibrocartilaginous discs between the bodies of the vertebrae prevent dis-
location.

The configuration of the skull (Pl. XXXII and Fig. 80) is
quite familiar in its entirety, but the fact that it is formed
by many bones may not be so obvious. The flat, slightly
curved cranial bones that encase the brain at the top, sides,
and back are capable of slight motion at birth. Hence the
shape of the head can be molded during delivery of the infant. But the bones soon become fused by denser fibrous tis-

sue and from that time on are incapable of further motion.

While the skull forms an excellent protection for the brain, it creates a very special problem when enlargement of the brain or its membranes requires an increase in space. Elsewhere in the body accommodation would be possible. In the skull even a fairly small hemorrhage, which would be of little importance in a distensible spot, may cause increase in intracranial pressure so that surgical release is necessary. By examining the eyes with an ophthalmoscope it is possible for a physician to see the head of the optic nerve, which changes in appearance if pressure within the skull is increased.

Like the skull, the numerous facial bones which form the stubby base of the nose, the arching cheekbones, the hollow orbit which protects each eye, and the maxilla, or upper jaw, are also fixed by fibrous joining. The mandible, or lower jaw, however, can move in several directions, up and down and, to a limited extent, in rotation with a grinding motion. It accomplishes this motion by virtue of the synovial joints (Fig. 81) on each side just in front of the ears, between the mandible and the cheek and upper jawbone.

The teeth can properly be considered part of the skeleton. Their roots are embedded in the jaws and are held in place by a firm fibrous membrane to which they are fixed by calcified cementum. Each tooth has a core of pulp which contains blood vessels and nerves. This is covered by dentine rich in calcium. The crown, that portion of the tooth which projects beyond the gum, is protected by the hardest substance in the body: enamel. The enamel is almost entirely calcium, with only about 1 to 2 per cent of organic matter. Enamel can withstand tremendous pressures. That is fortunate, for once enamel is damaged the body does not lay down any more to repair the defect. We have emphasized that there is a continuous turnover of minerals in the bones, but this is not true of the teeth. Interchange of calcium from the enamel is very slight.

The head is supported upon the upper or cervical vertebrae, which are the seven bones of the neck. The thoracic vertebrae are twelve in number, and have as many pairs of

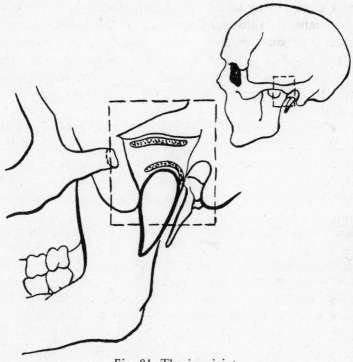

Fig. 81. The jaw joint.

ribs attached. The five lumbar vertebrae lie behind the abdomen. The sacrum and coccyx, five and four fused pieces respectively, form the midback of the pelvic cavity. The coccyx can be readily recognized as a vestigial tail.

Viewed from the side the spinal column presents gentle curvatures forward and backward, but not to either side.

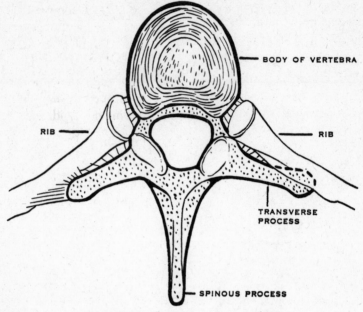

Fig. 82. Cross section of a vertebra.

When we speak of the spine as straight, we refer to its vertical character when seen or felt from the back.

The twenty-four separable pieces which form the movable part of the vertebral column are essentially alike in structure. Each forms a ring through which the spinal cord is threaded (Fig. 82). The front portion of the vertebrae is a very dense cylindrical mass. It provides the strength of the column and has no single marrow cavity. Marrow in the vertebrae is distributed in the crevices of the bony latticework which provides the rigidity.

The sides and back of the spinal ring are formed by thinner structures. Two transverse processes extend, one to each side. The spinous process in back is the part of the bone we can see, and feel with the fingers.

Between each of the vertebrae there is a compressible cushion of tough fibrous and cartilaginous tissue with a central pulpy nucleus. The slightly spongy character of these discs between the vertebrae allows limited bending and twisting in all directions, and compression with weight bearing. The discs are examples of fibrocartilaginous joints which have limited motion and are not bathed in synovial fluid.

The thoracic cage (Fig. 83) is formed by the vertebrae behind, by the sternum, or breastbone, in front, and by the twelve pairs of ribs curving around between them. The ribs are connected to the vertebrae and sternum by fibrocartilaginous joints so that expansion of the chest several inches can

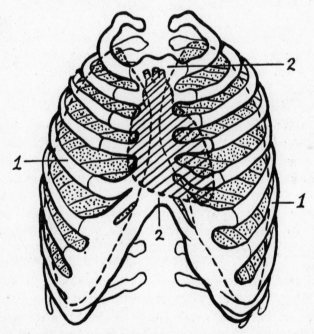

Fig. 83. The thoracic cage, sheltering the lungs and heart. 1. Ribs. 2. Sternum.

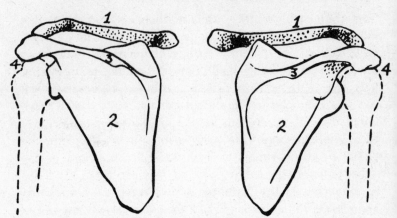

Fig. 84. The shoulder girdle (rear view). 1. Clavicle.
2. Scapula. 3. Spine of the scapula. 4. Shoulder joint.

occur. In youth some have a synovial membrane, which later disappears. The ribs are thin, flat structures which are more readily cracked than are most other bones.

The shoulder girdle (Fig. 84) is formed by a flat bone in back called the scapula and a narrow, riblike bone in front called the clavicle. These bones are popularly known as the shoulder blade and the collarbone. In a thin individual one can very easily see their contour, especially the spine of the scapula, a ridge running across its upper third. The clavicle attaches to the sternum in front and to an overhanging ledge on the scapula which forms part of the shoulder joint. The scapula is not fixed to bone at all and can move along with the arm, with which it forms a joint. Anyone who has watched the motions of the pitcher at a baseball game knows that this construction allows a wider range of motion than is possible at any other site in the body.

The arm has three long bones. The sturdy humerus forms the upper half, and its rounded head fits into a socket in the scapula as a clenched fist fits in the palm of the other hand.

Two thinner bones, the radius and ulna, together form the lower arm. The wrist has many small faceted bones, three of which form the condyloid structure which fits against the lower end of the radius and ulna (Pl. XXV). The pivot action apparent at the wrist is actually due to motion on each other of these two long bones.

One can easily see how many slender bones comprise the hand and fingers. Their numbers make possible the great flexibility and precision of motion which is necessary to a piano player or a watchmaker. The thumb is especially mobile because its metacarpal, or hand bone, stands off away from the others. One can touch thumb to little finger by moving from the wrist. All the joints of the extremities are synovial joints bathed in fluid contained within the synovial membrane. They differ only in the contour of their bony surfaces.

The pelvis (Fig. 85) is a strong, almost rigid structure.

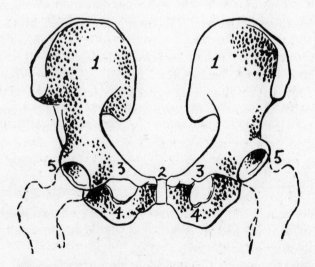

Fig. 85. The pelvis (front view). 1. Ilium. 2. Symphysis pubis. 3. Pubic bone. 4. Ischium. 5. Hip joint.

Swaying of the hips results from motion of the vertebrae and hip joint, but not from movement of the bones of the pelvis on each other. The largest pelvic bones are the iliacs, which form concave, fanlike structures attached to the sacrum behind by two fibrocartilaginous joints.

The pelvis is completed in front by a similar fibrocartilaginous joint, the symphysis pubis, between the two pubic bones. During childbirth there is a little give at this junction, but the pelvis is really very limited in its ability to expand. At this point in the body stability is required rather than flexibility.

The bones of the lower limbs are essentially similar to those of the arm, but differ in strength and relative size. The femur is the largest bone in the body. Its head forms a deep ball-and-socket joint with the pelvis. The knee joint between the femur and the two lower bones, the tibia and fibula, has directly in front an extra rounded bone, the patella. The small bones of the ankle and foot are adapted more for weight bearing than for facilitating the motion of the individual toes.

Ligaments. The skeleton as described above is only part of the body's frame. To be useful it must be supported at the joints by strong fibrous ligaments, so attached as to limit motion to the desired direction and keep the joint from becoming dislocated. However, ligaments must be flexible in order to permit some motion. They are tough, shiny, white tissue with a definite pattern of arrangement and specific attachments to bones.

When we bend or twist a joint beyond its normal extent, ligaments may be torn or stretched. The pain and disability that follow such accidents are considerable and muscle spasm rapidly appears in the area.

Muscle. Except for the pull of gravity, muscle is the agent of all motion in the body (Pl. XXVIII and Pl. XXIX). We have encountered muscle before in discussion of the heart and the alimentary tract. Muscles in these areas are involuntary and smooth, however. They differ in structure and behavior from the skeletal muscle that raises the arm and moves the foot. Skeletal muscle is voluntary and its fibers are striped, or striated (Pl. XXX and XXXI).

Muscle accomplishes its task by contracting to shorten the distance between its two points of attachment; by relaxing; and by maintaining tone. Contraction and relaxation are readily recognized. Tone is the state of tautness that exists when the muscles are not in motion. Even when we are asleep a degree of tone persists. Only in death or in certain types of paralysis is muscular relaxation complete.

Skeletal muscle is formed by bundles of long thin fibers which in turn have finer fibrillar divisions. The fiber is encased in a sheath, against which the nuclei of the muscles are closely applied. Crossbands, alternately appearing light and dark under the microscope, give the striated appearance from which the muscles' name is derived.

Most muscles attach to bones either directly or by long, dense, inelastic fibrous cords, the tendons (Fig. 86), which have great strength. You can see tendons moving on the back of your hand as you open and close your fist. A few muscles attach to the skin, as in the face, which has a striking voluntary mobility not found elsewhere in the body. We cannot change the expression of the skin of the arm or the chest as we can that of the face.

Voluntary muscle may also form a ring such as the sphincter about the anal opening. The tongue is voluntary muscle. It need not move bones, but its own movement is under the best control of any and, to our regret at times, it shows little fatigue.

From its attachments, its origin on the fixed bone, and its insertion on the bone it moves, one is tempted to try to determine what movement a muscle brings about when it contracts. But this is seldom possible. Motion of a part of the body in any direction is of necessity a group activity. The prime movers are the one or more muscles directly drawing the part in the desired direction. But the prime mover would be ineffectual if other muscles failed to hold the "fixed" part in place. These other muscles are called fixation muscles. There are also "antagonistic" muscles that must relax as

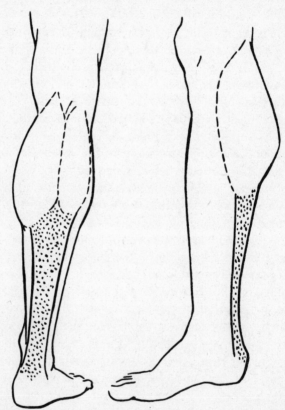

Fig. 86. The Achilles' tendons, indicated by shaded areas.

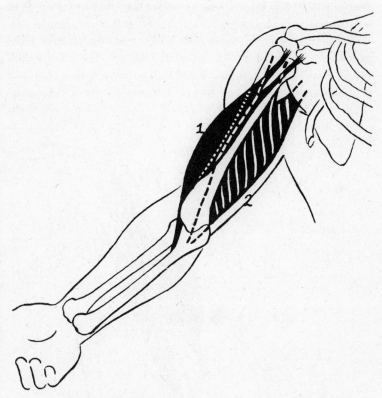

Fig. 87. The arm, elbow extended. 1. Biceps relaxed.
2. Triceps contracted.

the prime mover contracts; they are themselves the prime
movers when the action is reversed. And lastly, since few
muscles are capable of acting in only one direction, the
component effect which is not wanted in a particular movement must be counteracted by contraction of so-called synergetic muscles, or synergists.

Perhaps the best-known opposing muscles are the biceps
and triceps of the upper arm (Figs. 87, 88, 89). They

derive their names from the fact that they have two or three attachments, or heads, at their upper extremity; hence different components of the muscles can pull on different fixed points. In order to flex or bend the elbow, the biceps contracts with two other flexors, the brachialis and the brachioradialis. Since the biceps also supinates, or turns, the

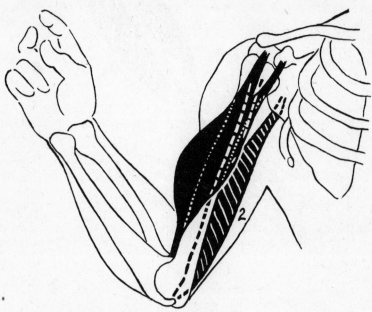

Fig. 88. The arm, elbow partly bent. 1. Biceps partly relaxed. 2. Triceps partly contracted.

hand over, this turning action must be opposed if it is not desired. And to enhance the strength of the contraction the fixation muscles of the shoulder must be rigidly tightened. We all recognize to what an extent clenching of the fist and contraction of the shoulder muscles contribute to our ability to make the biceps hard and protruding as it contracts.

The converse action, extension of the elbow with the triceps muscle now the prime mover, seems less complicated because it is usually a weaker motion. However, the triceps is not the only extensor, and fixation and synergetic action are also required.

Sometimes the co-ordinated muscle actions are at some distance from the moving part. When the finger is bent, the shoulder and entire arm must be held and the triceps and biceps become the fixation muscles. Other muscles must

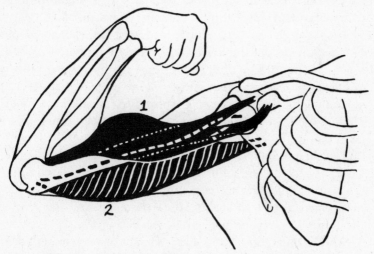

Fig. 89. The arm, elbow fully bent. 1. Biceps contracted. 2. Triceps relaxed.

prevent the wrist from bending; the synergists do this job, since they oppose that component of the flexors of the fingers. Relaxation of all these muscle contractions permits the closed fist to open. For complete straightening of the fingers the extensor muscles must contract.

Our own minds are unaware of single muscle action. We know how to perform a movement in which many co-ordinated muscles play a role, and we become skilled at such a movement by repetition. If injury to a muscle or paralysis of a nerve interferes with the use of certain muscles, it is often possible to re-educate remaining muscles to take over their action. The victim of poliomyelitis with residual muscle weakness or paralysis can commonly learn to perform well by substituting healthy muscle actions.

Muscles are held in relative position as they move by the broad membrane of fibrous tissue called fascia. Fascia is a supporting tissue to organs as well as to the framework, so that motion is controlled and contours are maintained.

About 75 per cent of muscle is water, and about 20 per cent is protein, but the fibril itself is mainly protein of various types. The most important protein responsible for the process of contraction is a complex called actomyosin. In the presence of the high-energy-containing substance adenosine triphosphate (ATP), actomyosin can change its shape and hence can contract or relax. ATP was previously discussed in relation to the production of energy in the chapter on metabolism (see page 90). Contraction of muscle fibers not only performs the work of motion, but also provides heat. Everyone recognizes that the way to keep warm is to move, and the greater the muscular activity the hotter we become.

Muscle fibers and fibrils alter their size over a period of time according to the amount of work performed. The bulging calf muscle of the active ballet dancer is an obvious example. The muscle has become hypertrophied, or enlarged. That same muscle would soon become withered or atrophic if the leg were paralyzed or if it were held in a cast. Perhaps the difference in the amount of blood flow in the active and inactive muscle determines its size in part.

THE HIGH WATER CONTENT of all the body's tissues is one of the prime requisites of life. Living tissues are never quiescent. At all times there is taking place some metabolic process for which the cells must be in a controlled fluid state. The regulation of water balance is a complicated matter which was previously touched on in discussions of elimination through the kidneys, intestine, and lungs (see pages 52, 68, and 83) and in the chapter on metabolism (see page 95).

The role of the skin in forming a container for the moist tissues cannot be overemphasized. The body is wet, but it must exist in air. The skin is the all-important barrier between the body's moisture and the air. When much of the body's surface has been lost by extensive burn, oozing of fluid from the exposed tissues may be one of the most serious effects of the injury.

The Epidermis. The outer layer of the skin, or epidermis (Fig. 90), is admirably adapted as a protective sheath. It consists everywhere of several layers of flattened cells, arranged in pavement fashion, to which the descriptive term, "stratified squamous epithelium," has been given. The constantly growing cells lie at the base of the epidermis, and from this they divide as they push outward toward the surface. As they push out they gradually change character, since all their nutrition must come from below. The epidermis has no blood vessels, as we can see when we receive a very superficial cut. Thus the outermost layers are actually dead cells with a high content of the protein keratin. As we go about our daily living these dead cells are constantly being rubbed off, so that we continuously shed our skin as it is just as continuously renewed from below.

Fig. 90. The skin and underlying connective tissue. 1. Epidermis. 2. Dermis. 3. Subcutaneous connective tissue.

We can readily see how this outermost skin layer varies in thickness in different parts of the body. Exposed parts such as the soles of the feet, which are commonly subject to trauma, have a thick outer shield of keratinized dead cells. When this condition occurs locally we speak of the areas as calluses.

Dense, highly keratinized dead tissue such as the nails or animal hoofs can become extremely hard and tough. Stratified squamous epithelium is also found in such parts of the body as the lining of the nose or mouth or vagina. As might be expected, there is little or no keratin in such relatively protected zones.

The skin owes its color in good part to the presence of a brown pigment, melanin, which is manufactured by special cells most abundant among the basal layer of epidermal cells. The amount of pigment is determined largely by heredity, but it is also markedly influenced by other factors, such as hormones and sunlight.

We are born with a tendency to some variation in the amount of pigment-forming cells in spots over the body. Exposure to ultraviolet light increases melanin formation in general (tanning), but especially in these pigment-forming spots (freckles). The pigment is protective, and those incapable of forming melanin in quantity tend to suffer sunburn more readily than does an individual with darker skin.

The two conditions which alter melanin production especially are pregnancy and adrenal-gland insufficiency. We have spoken of the brown nipples, and brown spots, especially on face and neck, which usually appear during pregnancy. These are reversible to a certain extent, but are apt to increase as the mother bears more children.

Melanin is known to be derived from tyrosine, one of the amino acids, which is also a precursor of adrenalin and noradrenalin. When the adrenals are the seat of extensive disease, more melanin often appears, in the skin and mucous membrane of the mouth. The mechanism for this increase is not clear, but there is some indication that the adrenal cortex acts as an inhibitor of melanin formation. Therefore the loss of adrenocortical activity could permit greater melanin formation. An individual with such loss, though a member of the white race, may become as dark as a mulatto. Often the abnormal pigmentation is patchy and may come and go.

Small benign tumors, or congenital malformations called pigmented moles, are found in almost everyone's skin. They remain as well-defined, raised or flat brown spots, which change little in size during life.

The Dermis. The deeper part of the skin, the dermis (Fig. 90), is a fibrous layer in which blood vessels, lymphatics, and nerves are numerous. The dermis also includes such epidermal

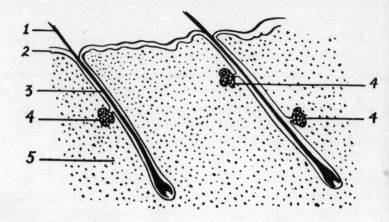

Fig. 91. Hair follicles and sebaceous glands. 1. Hair shaft. 2. Epidermis. 3. Hair follicle. 4. Sebaceous glands. 5. Dermis.

appendages as sweat glands, sebaceous glands, and hair follicles. All these structures play an important part in the well-being of the body as a whole; and through some of them, the nerve endings, man is helped to maintain his contact with the world around him.

The rich capillary network just beneath the epidermis is readily dilated or constricted according to the body's need to conserve warmth or to be cooled. When we step from a hot bath the whole body appears flushed due to the dilated surface capillaries. If it remains uncovered, the body rapidly cools as the increased amount of water eliminated as perspiration evaporates from the surface.

The lymphatics help carry away foreign particles which may penetrate the skin despite its compact epidermis. Bacteria and dirt are carried to the draining lymph nodes and hence rendered harmless to the body. Sometimes medications are injected in or beneath the skin. These are absorbed into the general circulation by lymphatics and capillaries.

Nerve endings are numerous and serve our need to be acutely aware of the position of each part of the body. All our co-ordinated movements depend upon such awareness. We need the sensation of pain to warn us of possible injury to a part. Where nerve sensitivity has been lost through disease, burns or other traumatic injuries are very prone to occur because of the insensitivity.

The hair follicles (Fig. 91), derived from the epidermis, form holders for the roots of the hair, and their epithelial linings give rise to the hair itself. Opening into each follicle are sebaceous glands which supply an oily substance to keep the skin soft, pliable, and more impermeable.

The sweat glands (Fig. 92) are situated deep in the dermis and have delicate ducts which penetrate through the surface epithelium. Perspiration is an excellent regulator of body temperature. When the healthy body is overheated, per-spiration is its mechanism for insuring a return to normal tem-

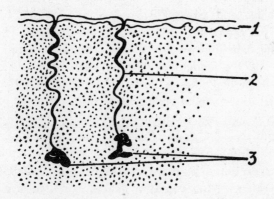

Fig. 92. Sweat glands. 1. Epidermis. 2. Ducts of sweat glands. 3. Sweat glands.

perature. The discharge of secretion from the sweat glands is an important adjunct to elimination of water and salts and must be taken into consideration in the body's water economy. In very hot weather, especially when a person is working in an environment such as a boiler room, his salt loss may be very debilitating, and may lead to muscle cramps. Drinking large quantities of water, of course, only depletes the body of more salt, and under some working conditions it is often necessary to take salt (sodium chloride) as well.

The subcutaneous tissue, a layer of fat under the skin, is not properly regarded as part of the skin itself, but it is of considerable aid in the conservation of heat. Women have a thicker fatty layer beneath their skin than do men. This is related to estrogen production and has a particular distribution which we recognize as the female form.

The regenerating powers of the skin are fortunately very great. A sharp knife cut heals rapidly by the formation of a clot in the line of cleavage and the growth of young fibrous tissue cells and surface epithelial cells across the narrow defect. But even when an area several inches across has been lost the deeper tissues fill the depression with capillaries and fibrous cells, and when the level of the surface has been reached the epidermis grows over from all sides. The sweat glands and hair follicles, however, do not form again in such an area and the amount of pigment may be different. With age the underlying tissue tends to contract and the resulting scar is a permanent record of the site of injury.

If skin is lost over so great an area that remaining tissues cannot replace it, a graft of skin can be planted effectively. That is, a thin layer of healthy skin can be removed from elsewhere on the body, often the thigh, and implanted on the denuded area. It too can grow along with the skin at the margin eventually to cover large segments of the body.

APPENDIX

ALIMENTARY—pertaining to the nutritive process

ANDROGEN—any hormone substance which promotes masculine characteristics

ANTIBODY—any of various specific substances produced in the body in counteraction to a specific foreign agent such as bacteria or bacterial poisons

ANTICOAGULANT—any substance which delays coagulation of the blood

CALIBER—the diameter of a canal or tube

CAPSULE—a fibrous or membranous envelope surrounding an organ or tissue

CARDIAC—pertaining to the heart

CARTILAGE—the translucent elastic substance attached to bones, forming parts of the skeleton and serving as connective tissue

CATALYST—an agent which accelerates a chemical reaction but itself remains virtually unchanged at the end of the process

CELL—any one of the minute masses that make up organized tissue, and consist, in the body, of cytoplasm containing a nucleus and circumscribed by a semipermeable membrane; the structural unit of plant and animal life

CEREBRAL—pertaining to the cerebrum, the main portion of the brain

CHROMOSOME—one of the small bodies which carry the hereditary unit, the gene, and which appear in the nucleus of a cell

CILIA—small hairlike processes found in some parts of the body, which by their constant movement propel various substances in one direction

COAGULANT—any agent that accelerates the clotting of blood

COLLAGEN—a gelatinlike protein that is an important constituent of some connective tissue

COMBUSTION—in the body, the uniting of chemical substances with oxygen, and the consequent production of heat

CONNECTIVE TISSUE—a special tissue which supports and binds together other tissues in nearly all parts of the body, so forming a framework for the organs, and composing the tendons, valves, capsules, and ligaments

CORTEX—the outer layer of an organ as distinguished from its inner substance

CRANIAL—pertaining to the cranium, or skull

CUSP—a tapering projection, as one of the segments of the aortic valve

DORSAL—pertaining to, or situated on the back, as of an organ or part

DUCT—a passage with distinct walls, especially a tube for the passage of excretions or secretions

DUCTULE—a very small duct

ELECTROLYTE—a substance, as an acid, base, or salt, that becomes a conductor of electricity when dissolved in a suitable fluid

EMBRYO—the unborn child in its earlier stages of development, usually during the first eight weeks

ENDOCRINE—secreting internally; applied especially to those

glands whose secretions pass directly into the blood or lymph

ENZYME—any of a group of organic compounds which by catalytic action accelerate changes in plant or animal material: they are not consumed in this process, and each is specific for a particular kind of substance

EPITHELIUM—a cellular tissue forming a sheet or membrane without fibers, such as the epidermis of the skin or mucous membrane of the stomach, or forming cords as in the liver

ESTROGEN—a generic term for the hormones responsible for female sexual characteristics

FETUS—the child in the womb, usually after the end of the eighth week

FIBRIL—a very small fiber or filament

FIBRINOGEN—a soluble protein in blood plasma which is one element in blood clotting

GASTRIC—pertaining to the stomach

GASTROINTESTINAL—pertaining to the stomach and intestine

GLAND—an organ that produces a specific substance or secretion

GROUND SUBSTANCE—a mucuslike fluid, filling tissue spaces throughout the body

GUSTATORY—pertaining to the sense of taste

HEPATIC—pertaining to the liver

HILLOCK—a small prominence

HILUM—a depression at that part of an organ where vessels and nerves enter

HORMONE—a chemical substance secreted into the body fluids by an endocrine gland, and which specifically influences the activities of other organs

HYDROSTATIC PRESSURE—a pressure exerted uniformly and perpendicularly to all surfaces, as by a homogenous fluid

INTERSTITIAL—pertaining to the spaces between the cellular elements of a tissue

LIGAMENT—a tough, fibrous band of tissue connecting bones or supporting viscera

LIPASE—a fat-splitting enzyme occurring in the liver, pancreas, stomach, and other digestive organs

LIPIDS—any one of a group of substances insoluble in water, and including fatty acids, fats, and sterols

LOBE—a somewhat rounded projection of an organ or part, as an ear lobe; a division of an organ marked off by a fissure on the surface, as a brain lobe

LOBULE—a small lobe, or a division of a lobe

LUMBAR—pertaining to the loins, the part of the human body on either side of the vertebral column between the five lower ribs and the hip bones

LYMPH—a transparent, slightly yellow liquid drained from intracellular spaces by special vessels

LYMPHATIC—a vessel conveying lymph

MEMBRANE—a thin, pliable layer of tissue which covers a surface or divides a space or organ

METABOLITE—any substance produced in the process of metabolism

MUCUS—the sticky, watery secretion produced by the mucous membranes, and which serves to moisten and protect them

MUSCULATURE—the muscular system of the body, or any part of it

NEURAL—pertaining to a nerve or nerves

NODE—a swelling or protuberance for some special purpose, as a lymph node

NUCLEUS—a small section within a cell, considered to be its essential part for growth and reproduction

OLFACTORY—pertaining to the sense of smell

ORGAN—any part or structure of the body which forms a distinct entity and is adapted for some specific function or functions: an organ is formed of two or more types of tissues grouped together in a definite pattern

OSMOTIC PRESSURE—the pressure produced by the passage of a solvent from the lesser to the greater concentration when two solutions are separated by a semipermeable membrane

OSSEOUS—bony

PERISTALSIS—the movement produced by wavelike contractions passing along a tubular muscle system

pH—the symbol used to indicate the measure of alkalinity and acidity in the body

PHAGOCYTE—a cell that ingests and destroys foreign material such as bacteria, suture threads, or cell fragments

PIGMENT—any normal or abnormal coloring matter of the body

PLASMA—the fluid part of the blood, without the corpuscles

PLEURAL—pertaining to the pleura, the membrane covering the lungs and lining the thoracic cavity

PROCESS—a projecting part

PULMONARY—pertaining to the lungs

REFLEX—an involuntary response in which an impulse evoked by a stimulus is transmitted along a nerve to a nerve center and from there passes along another nerve or nerves to start muscular or other activity

RH FACTOR—an agglutinating factor present in some types of human blood: the Rh factor (Rh is an abbreviation for rhesus) was first found in the blood of rhesus monkeys

SACRAL—pertaining to the sacrum, the bone which forms the posterior wall of the pelvis

SERUM—blood plasma from which fibrinogen has been removed

SINUS—a cavity, hollow space, or channel in the human body

SPASM—a sudden and violent contraction of a muscle or group of muscles

SPHINCTER—a strong circular band of muscle which encircles an orifice of the body and which can contract sufficiently to act as a closing

SPICULE—a small hard calcareous body serving as one of the elements of bone

STRIATED—striped or streaked

SUBCUTANEOUS—situated beneath the skin

SYNTHESIS—the building up of a more complex chemical compound by the union of simpler substances

SYSTEM—a group of organs and structures interrelated by behavior and all contributing toward one vital function of the body

TENDON—a tough cord of specialized connective tissue which unites a muscle with some other part and transmits the force the muscle exerts

THORACIC—pertaining to the chest

TISSUE—an aggregate of cells similarly specialized and united in a specific behavior

TONE—the proper degree of tension of the tissues and organs of the body

TRAUMA—a bodily injury produced by some extrinsic or abnormal intrinsic agent

TROPHIC—of or pertaining to nutrition: it is specifically used as an ending for names of the anterior pituitary hormones which have specific stimulating effect on other endocrine glands

TUBULE—any small tube

VALVE—a membranous fold or other structure in a canal or passage which prevents the reflux of its contents, as with the valves which guard the entrances to the aorta and pulmonary arteries

VASCULAR—pertaining to vessels, such as those which carry blood and lymph

VENTRAL—situated on the abdominal side of the body; pertaining to, or situated on, the anterior or lower surface, as of an organ or part; the opposite of dorsal

VESSEL—any canal for transporting a fluid such as blood or lymph

VILLI—tiny processes such as are found on the inner surfaces of the small intestine, where they absorb nutriment

VITAMIN—any of a group of food factors essential in small quantities to maintain life and insure normal metabolic functioning of the body, but not in themselves supplying energy

BIBLIOGRAPHY

AMBERSON, W. A. D. *Pathology,* 2nd ed. St. Louis: C. V. Mosby Co., 1953.

CUNNINGHAM, D. J. *Textbook of Anatomy,* 9th ed., ed. by J. C. Brash. New York: Oxford, 1951.

FULTON, JOHN F. *Textbook of Physiology.* Philadelphia: W. P. Saunders, 1950.

GAMBLE, JAMES L. *Chemical Anatomy, Physiology and Pathology of Extracellular Fluid.* Cambridge: Harvard University Press, 1953.

GOODMAN, LOUIS and ALFRED GILMAN. *The Pharmacological Basis of Therapeutics,* 2nd ed. New York: Macmillan, 1955.

GRANT, J. C. B. *An Atlas of Anatomy,* 3rd ed. Baltimore: Williams and Wilkins, 1951.

HAM, ARTHUR W. *Histology,* 2nd ed. Philadelphia: Lippincott, 1953.

HARRISON, T. R. *Principles of Internal Medicine,* 2nd ed. New York: Blakiston, 1954.

PASCHKIS, KARL E. and others. *Clinical Endocrinology.* New York: Hoeber, 1954.

PATTEN, BRADLEY M. *Human Embryology,* 2nd ed. New York: Blakiston, 1953.

STRONG, OLIVER S. and ADOLPH ELWYN. *Human Neuroanatomy,* 3rd ed. Baltimore: Williams and Wilkins, 1953.

WEST, EDWARD S. and WILBERT R. TODD. *Textbook of Biochemistry.* New York: Macmillan, 1950.

INDEX

A

ACTH............101, 104, 105, 106
ATP....................... 90, 91, 200
Abdominal cavity 56, 63, 115;
  during pregnancy 124, 138-9
Abducens (7th cranial) nerve,
  161, 166
Achilles' tendon, *see* Tendons
Acid-base balance 53, 61, 84,
  96, 108
Acidosis 53, 108
Acromegaly 102
Actomyosin 200
"Adam's Apple", *see*
  Thyroid cartilage
Addison's disease 104
Adenosine triphosphate,
  see ATP
Adrenal cortex 96, 104-5, 203
Adrenal gland 10, 67, 79, 82,
  98, *103*, 103-6
Adrenal medulla 104, 105-6
Adrenalin 13, 22, 104, 105-6,
  203
Adrenocortical hormones, 92,
  96, 105, 106
Adrenocorticotrophin, *see*
  ACTH

Air pressure, *see* Hearing,
  Lungs
Alar *39*
"Alarm reaction", *see*
  Adrenalin
Albumin.................... 33, 74, 77
Alcohol and alcoholism. 82, 119
Aldosterol 105
Alimentary tract, 54-71; *see*
  also Mouth, Esophagus,
  Stomach, Small intestine,
  Pancreas, Large intestine
Alkalinity 60, 61, 96
Allergic states 30
Alveolus *48*, 49, 140
Amino acids: in plasma, 33;
  and digestion, 67, 68; and
  protein metabolism, 89,
  91, 92; and skin pigments,
  203
Amniotic sac, *135*, 135-6,
  137, 141
Amphiarthroses 186
Amylase 67
Anabolism 89
Androgen 118
Anemia 29, 139
Anesthesia, general 38

Animal experimentation: in endocrinology, 99, 101, 102, 107, 108; in cell differentiation, 136; in eye studies, 167

Ankle 194

Anti-anemic principle, see Liver

Antibacterial drugs 70

Antibodies 31, 34

Anticoagulant drugs 33

Antithrombin 32

Anus 70, 71, 131

Anvil, see Incus

Anxieties, see Emotions

Aorta, 12, 17, 18, 19, 44, 57; see also Heart, Circulatory system

Aortic valve 15, 16, 16

Appendix 69, 70

Aqueous fluid 167, 168

Areolar glands 139

Arm 186, 192-3, 197, 198, 199, 199

Arteries 18-20; see also Circulatory system

Arterioles 19, 20, 21

Arteriosclerosis 171

Arthrodia 187

Ascheim-Zondek test 134

Association areas, see Brain

Asthma 45

Astigmatism 170

Atmospheric air, see Breathing

Atrioventricular node 13

Atrioventricular valves, see Mitral valve, Tricuspid valve

Atrium 12-14, see also Heart

Audition, see Hearing

Auditory nerve 173

Auditory receptive center 157

Auricle, see Atrium, Ear

Autonomic nervous system, 148-9, 163

Axon 144, 144, 145, 145, 153, 159

B

Baby, development of....136-139

Bacteria 29, 30, 31, 44, 61, 70, 71, 204

Balance, see Equilibrium

Ball and socket joints 187

Banting 107

Basal metabolism, see Metabolism rate

Basophil, see White blood cells

Belching, see Cardia

Best 107

Bicarbonate, see Salts, Sodium

Biceps 163, 197, 197, 198, 198, 199, 199

Bile 26, 65, 75, 76; acids, 95; ducts, 72, 76; pigments, 76; salts, 67, 68, 76

Biliary passages 77-78

Bilirubin 76, 78

Binocular vision, see Stereoscopic vision

Birth 137, 140-42

Bladder, see Urinary bladder

Blastocyst 132

Blood: acidity of, 53; agglutination, 35; and body conditions, 26; carries fatty acids, 94; carbon dioxide in, 28, 52; clotting, 32, 33, 74-5; fetal, 134; groups, 34-35; hemoglobin in, 28, 29; and liver, 73, 77; oxygen in, 28, 52; plasma, 25, 28, 33-34, 79, 82; platelets, 26, 31-2; portal, 73; red cells, 26, 27, 28, 29, 75; regulated by kidneys, 79-80; white cells, 26, 29-30, 37

Blood count 31

Blood donors, see Blood groups

Blood pressure 21-23, 107, 171; hydrostatic and osmotic, 36

"Blue baby" 137

Bone 164, 182-5, 183; see also Skeleton

Bone marrow 4, 26, 29, 76, 182, 183, 190

Brachialis and brachioradialis 198

Brain 7, 142, 144, 146, 155, 162-3; association areas of, 159, 180; in embryo, 137; metabolism of, 150; and vision, 171

Breakdown products, see Metabolites

Breastbone 26, 44, 191, 191, 192

Breasts, female 110, 129, 130; see also Mammary glands

Breathing: artificial 38; normal 50, 50, 51, 52

Breech presentation 137

Bronchi and bronchial tree 39, 43, 44, 45, 46

Bronchiole, see Small bronchi

Bulbo-urethral gland 121, 123

Bundle of His 13

C

Calcium 32, 34, 69, 95, 96, 113, 114, 177; 183, 185, 188; carbonate, 56; crystals in ear, 177; phosphate, 55

Calluses 202

Camera, and eye 166, 167

Cancer: of pancreas, 108; of pituitary gland, 103; of testes, 116

Capillaries, 20; bile, 76; liver, 76; nose, 40; see also Circulatory system

Carbohydrates 33, 34, 89, 92

Carbon dioxide 28, 38, 52, 53, 90, 96

Carbon monoxide 29

Carbonates 34

Cardia 58

Cardiovascular system, see Heart, Circulatory system, Lungs, Lymphatics

Cartilage, 186; cricoid, 43; of septum, 39; thyroid, 43

Catabolism 89

Cataract 168

Cecum 69, 70

Cell, 2, 5, *5*, 6, 7, 11; agglutination, 35; blood, 25-35, 37; bone, 183, *184;* division, 6, 7; differentiated, 7; embryonic development of, 136; intestinal lining, 68; kidney, 80, 83; male sex, 115; mast, 30; nerve, 144-6; pigment-forming, 203; Purkinje system in heart, 13; reticuloendothelial, 76
Cementum 188
Central lobular vein 74
Central nervous system, 149-160; *see also* Brain, Spinal cord
Cerebellum *155*, 155-6, 159
Cerebral cortex *145*, 154, 157, 158, 160
Cerebral hemispheres 156, *157*
Cerebrospinal fluid 150
Cerebrum 156, *157*
Cerumen 173
Cervix *125*, 129, 130, *135*, 141
Cheekbones 188
Chewing 55, 58, 161
Childbirth, *see* Birth
Chlorides, 34, 69; *see also* Salts
Cholesterol 33, 76, 95
Chordae tendineae 15, 16
Chorioid *167*
Chromosomes, 119, 136; *see also* Genes
Chyme 61, 62, 65, 67
Cilia: in bronchi, 46; in epididymis, 119; in Fallopian tubes, 128; in nose, 40, 42; in trachea, 44
Circulatory system: arteries, 18-20; capillaries, 19-20; circulation, 17-22, *18;* dynamics of, 20-21; heart, 12-17; lungs, 11, 12; veins, 19-20
Circumcision 123
Clavicle *192*, 192
Clitoris *131*, 131
Coagulation, *see* Blood clotting
Coccyx 189
Cochlea *175*, 176
Cochlear (8th cranial) nerve, 162, 176
Coffee 82
Cold, sensation of 154, 159, 164
Collagen 8, 45, 51
Collarbone, *see* Clavicle
Collip 107
Colon, *see* Large intestine
Color blindness and vision 169, 170
Colostrum 142
Compound E, *see* Cortisone
Compound F, *see* Hydrocortisone
Conception, *see* Fertilization
Cones 169, 170
Connective tissue .8, *9*, 8, 9, 10
Copper 75
Cornea 167-8, *167*
Coronary arteries 17
Corpus cavernosum 87, 122
Corpus hemorrhagicum 127
Corpus luteum 128, 129
Corpus spongiosum 87, 122
Cortisone 105

Cough reflex 45
Cranial bones 187
Cranial cavity 149, 171
Cretin 110
Cystic duct 77
Cytoplasm 5, 6

D

Daughter cells, see Cell division
Deafness 174, 176
Decidua 134
Dendrite 144, 144, 145, 145, 158
Dentine 188
Defecation 71
Depot fat, see Fat storage
Dermatomes 163, 164
Dermis 202, 203-4, 204, 205
Diabetes insipidus 83, 102, 103
Diabetes mellitus 83, 102, 106, 171
Diabetics 94, 107
Diaphragm 50, 51, 58
Diarrhea 97
Diarthroses 186
Diastole 14, 15, 17, 19, 21
Diet, high protein or fat 76
Digestion: in mouth, 55, 56; in stomach, 58-62; in small intestine, 62-65
Dihydrotachysterol 114
Discs, vertebral 187, 191
Dogs, see Animal experimentation
Ductless glands 98
Duodenum 58, 62, 63, 65, 67, 77
Dura mater 149

E

Ear, 162, 173, 173-4; drum, 173, 173, 174; external, 173, 173; inner, 173, 173, 174, 175, 176; middle, 173, 173, 174, 174; and equilibrium, 176
Eating habits 54
Egg, see Ova
Ejaculation 123
Ejaculatory ducts 86, 87, 121
Elastin 8
Elbow 197, 198, 199, 199
Electrocardiogram 13
Electrocortin, see Aldosterol
Electrolyte metabolism 95-97
Embryo, 7, 134, 135, 136-9; male, 115; female, 126; see also Fetus
Emotional stimuli 22, 104-5
Emotions: and bile, 77; and body, 154; and intestinal system, 71; and nervous system, 148; during pregnancy, 135; and stomach, 62; and taste, 158; types of, 158
Enamel 188
Endocrine glands 11, 98-114, 184
Endometrium 129, 130
Endothelium 3
Energy and synthesis, 90-92, 94, 107; see also Proteins, Enzymes
Environmental stress 104-5
Enzymes, 6, 55, 89, 90-92; in kidneys, 83; in liver, 93; in nerve synapse, 145;

Enzymes—*Continued*
in pancreas, 67-70; in plasma, 34; in stomach, 58-62; in small intestine, 62-65; *see also* Amylase, Lipases, Lipids, Pepsin, Ptyalin, Rennin, Thrombin, Trypsin
Eosonophil, *see* White blood cells
Epidermis 201, *202*, *204*, *205*, 206
Epididymis *117*, 118, 119, *121*
Epiglottis *42*, *43*, 43, 178
Epinephrine, *see* Adrenalin
Epithelium: in ovaries, 126, 130; stratified squamous, of skin, 201; types of, 2, 3; in urinary bladder, 86
Equilibrium 156, 161, 162, 176-7
Erythrocyte-maturing factor 29
Esophagus 42, 44, 56-7, *57*
Estrogen 75, 110, 127, 129, 134, 142, 206
Eunuch 118
Eustachian tube *41*, 174
Evolution, animal 95
External genitalia, female, 86; *see also* Vagina, Vulva
Extracellular fluid 95-7
Eye, *165*, 165-9, *166*, 166, *172*, 176; ball, 161, 165, 171; infant's, 141; lashes, 165; lid, 161, 165, *167*

F

F. S. H. 109, 126
Facial (7th cranial) nerve, 161-2, 175, 180

Fallopian tubes 124, *125*, 128, 129, 132, *133*
Farsightedness 170
Fascia 200
Fat, 33, 67, 74, 75, 76; and energy, 91; metabolism, 93-94; storage, 94
Fatty acids 67, 68, 93-4
Feces 69, 70, 77, 78
Female reproductive organs 119, 124, *125*, 125-31
Femoral nerve 164
Femur *183*, 194
Fertilization 128, 132, *133*
Fetus, 116, 119, 129, 134, 137, *138*, 139; *see also* Embryo
Fibrin, *see* Blood clotting
Fibrinogen 32, 33, 74
Fibroblasts and fibrocytes 9, 10
Fibula 194
Fingers 186, 193, 199
Follicle-stimulating hormone, *see* F. S. H.
Food: absorption, 68-70; and energy, 91; intake, 40; and metabolism, 89; salivary reaction to, 55; storage, 54; and taste, 177-8; and vitamin-B, 61
Foot 194
Freckles 203
Frontal bone 187
Frontal lobe *155*, *157*, 158
Frontal lobotomy 158

G

Gallbladder 72, 77
Gametes 110
Gametogenic hormone 109

Ganglia 146, 149, 153, 154, 158, 162, 163

Gastric juice 55, 59, 60, 61

Gastritis 60

Gastrointestinal disturb-
ances 107

Genes, 5; see also Chromosomes

Gestation, see Pregnancy

Glans penis 87, 123

Glia 146

Globulins 33

Glomerulus 82, 83, 88

Glossopharyngeal (9th cranial) nerve, 162, 180

Glucose, 90-91; see also
Sugar

Glycerol 67, 68

Glycogen 74

Goiter 112

Gonadotrophins, 101, 109;
chorionic, 134

Gonads 101, 109-10

Graafian follicle 126, 127, 127

Gray matter, see Brain,
Spinal cord, Cerebral cortex

Groin, 119; see also Pelvis

Ground substance 9, 183

Growth hormone 101-2

Guinea pigs, see Animal experimentation

Gustatory sense, see Taste

Gyri 156-7

H

Hair: female genital, 131;
follicles, 204, 205, 206;
male body, 109; nose, 40,
180

Hammer, see Malleus

Hand bone 187, 193

Haversian canals 183

Head, 176, 185; see also
Equilibrium, Skull

Headaches 148

Hearing 159, 161, 162, 172-5

Heart: and aorta, 12;
"beats", 12, 13; and calcium deficiency, 97; cham-
bers of, 12; and circula-
tory system, 11; diastole
and systole, 14; failure,
74; growth of, 7; and hy-
perthyroidism, 112; loca-
tion of, 12; and nervous
system, 148, 149; Pur-
kinje system, 13; rate, 13;
valves of, 15

"Heartburn", see Cardia

Heat: conservation and skin,
206; production of, see
Energy, Metabolism rate;
sensation of, 154, 159

Hemoglobin 28, 29

Heparin 30, 75

Hepatic artery 74

Hepatic duct 77

Hepatic veins 75

Hereditary factors, see Genes

Hilum 72, 76

Hipbone 26

Hormones: body routes of,
11, 67; and liver, 75; and
protein synthesis, 93;
types of trophic, 93; see
also ACTH, Adrenalin,
Adrenocortical, Aldos-
terol, Androgen, Corti-

Hormones—*Continued*
  sone, Dihydrotachysterol,
  Endocrine glands, Estro-
  gen, F. S. H., Female re-
  productive, Gametogenic,
  Gonadotrophin, Growth
  hormone, Hydrocortisone,
  I. C. S. H., Insulin, L. H.,
  Lactogen, Norepinephrine,
  Parathormone, Pitocin,
  Pitressin, Pituitary, Pos-
  terior pituitary, Proges-
  terone, Steroids, Thyroid,
  Testosterone
Humerus 192
Hunger 156, 157
Hydrochloric acid 60, 61
Hydrocortisone 10, 105
Hydrostatic pressure 36
Hymen *131*, 131
Hyoid bone *111*
Hyothyroid membrane *111*
Hyperthyroidism 112, 113
Hypoglossal (12th cranial)
  nerve 162
Hypothalamus 148, 156

I

I. C. S. H. 109
Ileum *62*, 63, 64, 68, 70
Ilium *193*, 194
Images, *see* Sight
Incus *174*, 174
Inferior vena cava 14, 19, 74
Insulin 67, 91, 107-8
Insulin shock 107
Internal genital organs, fe-
  male, *see* Fallopian tubes,
  Ovaries, Uterus

Interstitial cell-stimulating
  hormone, *see* I. C. S. H.
Iodine 112
Ions 69
Iris *166*, *167*, 168, 169
Iron 28, 29, 69, 75
Ischium *193*
Islets of Langerhans *66*, 67, 107

J

Jaundice 78
Jawbone, *see* Mandible
Jejunum *62*, 63, 64, 68
Joints: ball and socket, 187,
  194; condyloid, 186-7;
  fibrocartilagenous, 191;
  hinge, 186; hip, 187, *193;*
  jaw, *189;* knee, 194; and
  peripheral nerves, 164;
  saddle, 186-7; shoulder,
  187, *192;* synovial, 186,
  187, 193

K

Keratin 202
Ketone bodies 94
Kidney, 7, *26*, *63*, 79-84, *80*,
  84, *85*, 96; and eye tis-
  sues, 171
Knee 186
Krause's end-bulb 164

L

L.H. 109, 128
Labia majora *125*, 131, *131*
Labia minora *125*, 131, *131*
Labor, 103, 140-42; *see also*
  Birth

Lacrimal duct and gland *165*, 165

Lactation 142

Lactic acid 90

Lactogen 142

Landsteiner, *see* Blood groups

Large intestine *69*, 70-71

Larynx 39, *42*, 43

Lecithin 76, 94

Lens *166*, *167*, 168-9

Leucocytes, *see* White blood cells

Leucocytosis 31

Leydig cells 109, 118

Ligaments 182, 194

Light 169-170, 171, 203

Lipases 60, 67

Lipids 33, 95

Liver 7, 26, 29, 32, 61, *63*, 64, 72-78, *73*, 94, 106

Lumbar puncture 150

Lumbar vertebrae 189

Lungs, 11, 12, 37, 38, 39, 45, 46, 47-51, *47*, *48*, 52; in embryo, 137

Luteinizing hormone, *see* L.H.

Lymphatics: glands, 37; nodes, 24, 30, 31, 36, 37, 44; system, 19, *23*, 24, 35-7, 94; vessels, *23*, 203-4

Lymphocytes, *see* White blood cells

Lysozyme 166

M

Macrophages 31

Magnesium 184

Male: adult changes, 109, reproductive system, 115-123; sex cells, 116; sex characteristics, 118

Malleus *173*, *174*, 174

Mammary glands 139-140, *139*, 142

Mandible *187*, 188

Mast cells 30

Mastication, *see* Chewing

Maxilla *187*

Medulla oblongata 148, *151*, 154, *155*, 156, 160, 180

Megakaryocytes 32

Meissner's corpuscles 164

Melanin 202

Memory, 159-60; of smell, 181; of taste, 180

Meninges 149

Menopause 110, 125, 130

Menstruation, 126-7, 129-30, 131; cessation during pregnancy, 134; after pregnancy, 142

Mesentery 63

Mesothelium 3

Metabolism rate 91

Metabolites 73, 93

Metacarpal bone, *see* Hand bone

Midbrain 156, 160, 180

Minerals: *see* Calcium, Chlorides, Copper, Iron, Magnesium, Phosphorus, Salts, Sodium

Mitosis, *see* Cell division

Mitral valve 12, 14, *15*, 15

Moles 203

Monocyte, *see* White blood cells

Monosaccharides 68

Mother's milk 142

Motion 156

Motor-end plate 164

Motor nerves, 147, 150; *see also* Nervous system

Motor neurons, *see* Neurons

Motor projection center......*157*

Motor root, *see* Spinal nerve roots

Motor tracts, *see* Tracts

Mouth 43, 44, 55, 56

Mucin 60

Mucous membrane: in large intestine, 70; in gallbladder, 77; in nose, 40, 181; in small intestine, 64, 94; in stomach, 58; in trachea, 44

Mucus, *see* Mucous membrane, Secretions

"Mumps", *see* Parotid glands

Muscle, skeletal 109, 163-4, 176, 182, 194-5, 196, 197, 198, 199, 200

Muscle cramps 206

Muscle tissue *3*

Musculocutaneous nerve 163

Myelin 146, *147*

Myotomes 163

N

Nails 202

Nasal cavities *41*

Nasal duct *165*

Nasal infection and sprays, *see* Nose

Nearsightedness 170

Nephrons 80, *81*, 82

Nerve cells, *see* Neurons

Nerve process 144, *144*

Nerve sensitivity in skin 205

Nerve transmission 144-45

Nerve trunks 145, 146, 160

Nervous system, 11, 22, 105, 106, 135, 143-64; functions of, 147-9; subdivisions of, 144-6

Neurons, 144, 145, 158; associative, 150; motor, *144*, 147; sensory, *146*, 147, 150

Neutrophil, *see* White blood cells

Nipple *139*, 140

Nitrogen: in air, 38; in protein, 92

Noradrenalin (norepinophrine) 22, 105-106, 203

Nose *39*, 40, *41*, 43, 161

Nuclei: of cells, 5; muscle, 93; nerve, 146, 156, 161

Nursing, *see* Lactation

Nutrition: and liver, 74; prenatal, 135, 138; of skin, 202; *see also* Food

Nutritional disturbances 107

O

Occipital cortex 161

Occipital lobe *157*, 159, 161, 171, *172*

Ocular muscles, 166; *see also* Eye

Oculomotor (3rd cranial) nerve 161, 166

Odors, *see* Smell

Olfactory bulb 161, 180, 181

Olfactory (1st cranial) nerve, 160-61, 180, *181*

Omentum *63*, 64

Optic (2nd cranial) nerve 161, *167*, 169, 171, *172*, 188

Organs, structure of 7

Orgasm 123, 132

Osmotic pressure 36

Osteoid 183

Ova 109, 110, 124, 125, 126, *128*, 128, 129, 132, *133*, 134

Ovaries, 98, 109, 110, 124, 125-8, *125, 127, 133*, 136; *see also* Gonads

Ovulation, 127, 132, 142; *see also* Menstruation

Oxygen: in air, 38; and glucose, 90; in hemoglobin, 28; in lungs, 52; and metabolism, 89; in respiratory system, 38; *see also* Circulatory system

P

Pacinian body 164

Pain 154, 158-9, 205

Palate 56

Pancreas *65, 66*, 65-70, 98, 106-7, 108

Papillary muscle 15

Parasites 30

Parasympathetic nerve 149

Parathormone 114

Parathyroid gland 84, 98, 112-14, *113*, 184-5

Parietal bone *187*

Parietal lobe *157*, 159, 180

Parotid glands 55

Patella 194

Pelvis and pelvic cavity 124, 185, 189, *193*, 193-4

Penicillin 83

Penis 86, *87*, 109, *116, 120, 121*, 122-3

Pepsin 59, 60

Peptones 60

Pericardium 12, 48

Periosteum 182, 183

Peripheral nerve *147*

Peripheral nervous system 145, 160-164

Peristalsis: bronchi, 46; esophagus, 57; and nervous system, 149; small intestine, 64; stomach, 58; ureter, 85

Peritoneum, *63*, 64, 86; female, 124; male, 115

Perspiration 148, 204, 205

pH, *see* acid-base balance

Phagocytes and phagocytosis 29, *30*, 31

Pharynx, 39, 40, *41, 56;* and hearing, 174-5; and taste, 178

Phenol red 83

Phospholipids 33, 94

Phosphorus 34, 69, 84, 113, 184, 185

Pia arachnoid 149, 150

Pia mater 149, 150

Pigments 170, 202-203, 206

Pitocin 102, 103

Pitressin 102, 103

Pituitary gland 4, 82, 98, *100*, 100-102, 103, 128, 142, *155*, 156; anterior, 100-101, 103, 104, 106, 109, 111; posterior, 101-103

Pituitary hormones 83, 96

Placenta 134-5, *135, 138,* 140, 141-2

Plasma, *see* Blood

Platelets 26, *31,* 32

Pleura *47,* 48

Pleurisy 48

Plexuses: brachial and lumbosacral 163

Poliomyelitis 200

"Polys" (polymorpho-nuclear cells) 29, 30

Pons ... 154, *155,* 155, 156, 160

Portal vein 68, 73, 74

Position sense 154, 159

Potassium, 95, 96; *see also* Salts

Pre-Cambrian Era 95

Pregnancy 124, 128, 132-42

Premature birth 140, 141

Prenatal influence 135

Primitive sex cells, *see* Ova, Sperm

Progesterone 110, 128, 129-30, 134

Prostate gland 86, *87,* 109, *120,* 120-21, *121,* 122, 123

Protein: in cytoplasm, 6; breakdown of, 93; digestion of, 59-70; in male muscles, 93; metabolism, 89, 92-93; in plasma, 33, 36; in skeletal muscle, 200; synthesis, 93

Prothrombin 32, 75, 77

Protoplasm 89

Protoses 60

Psyche, adult changes 109

Psychosomatic manifestations 148

Puerperium 142

Pus 175

Ptyalin 55, 60

Puberty 109, 118, 122, 125, 126, 129, 140

Pubic bone *193,* 194

Pulmonary artery 17

Pulmonary valve 14-17

Pulmonary vein 18

Pulse, *see* Heart rate

Pupil *161, 166,* 169

Purkinje system 13

Pylorus 61, 62

R

Rabbits, *see* Animal experimentation

Radial nerve 164

Radiation exposure 119

Radioactive matter 92, 184

Radius 186, 193

Rats, *see* Animal experimentation

Reasoning 158

Rectum *69,* 70, 71, 122

Red blood cells........*26,* 27-9, 75

Reflexes, 143, 147-8, 152; eye, 165, 169; cough, 45; knee-jerk, *148,* 152; salivary, 55

Refraction, light 168

Relay stations, 145, 152; *see also* Nerve transmission, Spinal cord

Rennin 60

Repair processes, *see* Tissue

Reproductive system: female, 124-31; male, 115-23; and peritoneum, 64

Respiratory system, 4, 38-53, 148-54; *see also* Breathing

Reticulin fibers 8, 9

Reticuloendothelial cells 76

Retina 161, *166, 167,* 169-71

Rh factor 35

Rhesus monkey 35

Ribs 26, 44, *190,* 191

Rickets 185

Rods 169, 170

Ruffini, corpuscles of 164

S

Saccule 177

Saliva 55, 60, 162

Salivary glands 55

Salts, 96; absorbed in intestine, 69; in bone, 183; loss of through skin, 206; in saliva, 55

Scapula *192,* 192

Scar tissue 9, 206

Sciatic nerve 164

Sclera *167*

Scrotum *87,* 115, *116,* 116, *121*

Sebaceous glands 173, *204,* 204, 205

Secretin 67

Secretion granules 6

Secretions, stomach 60-62

Semen 119, 120, 122, 123

Semicircular canals .. *175,* 176

Seminal vesicles 86, 120, *121,* 123

Sensations, in nervous system 154, 158

Sensory center, *see* Thalamus

Sensory nerves 147, 162

Sensory neurons, *see* Neurons

Sensory root, *see* Spinal nerve root

Sensory tracts, *see* Tracts

Septum *39*

Sex characteristics: in embryo, 136; female, 126, 129; male, 118

Sex hormones, *see* Androgen, Estrogen, Progesterone, Steroids, Testosterone

Sexual intercourse 131, 132

Shoulder: blade, *see* Scapula; girdle, 186, *192;* joint, *192;* muscle, 100

Sight 161, 165-71

Sigmoid flexure *69,* 70

Silver nitrate 141

Sino-atrial node 13, 14

Sinuses 40, *41*

Skeleton 109, 114, 184, 185-94

Skin 201-6, *202;* grafting, 206; of infant, 141; sensations in nervous system, 162, 163, 164; and water evaporation, 52

Skull *187,* 187-9

Sleep 45, 156; feigning, 166

Small bronchi 39, 45, *48,* 49

Small intestine, 61, *62,* 62-5, *63,* 68; embryonic devel-

Small intestine—*Continued* opment of, 136; and nervous system, 149

Smell, sense of 161, 178, 180-1

Smith, Dr. Philip 101

Sodium: bicarbonate, 28, 95; chloride, 95, 166, 184; elimination of, 84; in plasma, 34; *see also* Salts

Solar plexus 149

Somatic nervous system 148, 149

Sound: in vocal cords, 43; waves, 173

Sperm 116, 118, 119, 122, 126, 132; *see also* Spermatozoa

Spermatic cord *116,* 119-20

Spermatozoa 109, 110, 119, 120, *121,* 130, 132, *133; see also* Sperm

Sphenoid bone *187*

Sphincter muscles: anal 71, 195; iris, 169; urethral, 88

Spicules, bone 182

Spinal accessory (11th cranial) nerve 162

Spinal column 185, 187, 189-90

Spinal cord 26, 51, 145, 146, 147-8, *148,* 149, 150, *151,* 152, *153, 155,* 159, 162-4

Spinal nerve roots 145, 152, 160, 162

Spinal nerves *153*

Spinal zones 150, *151*

Spleen 27, *27,* 31, *63,* 64, 76

Staining dyes 29, 30

Stapes *174,* 174

Starch 55, 60; *see also* Digestion

Stereoscopic vision .. 171, *172*

Sterility and fertility 118, 128

Sternum, *see* Breastbone

Steroids 95, 105, 109, 110

Sterols 93-4, 95

Stirrup, *see* Stapes

Stomach 55, 56, 58-62, *59, 63,* 64

Stool, *see* Feces

Strangulation 38, 44

Subarachnoid space 150

Sublingual glands 55

Submaxillary glands 55

Sugar 33, 55, 68, 74, 90, 106, 108

Sugar diabetes, *see* Diabetes mellitus

Sulci 156-7

Sulfates 69

Sunburn 203

Superior vena cava 14, 19

Supplemental and tidal air ... 51

Swallowing 43, 45, 56, 57, 162, 174

Sweat glands 205, *205,* 206

Sweating, *see* Perspiration

Swollen glands, *see* Lymph nodes

Sympathetic nerve 149

Symphysis pubis *193,* 194

Synapse 145

Synarthroses 186

Synergists, *see* Muscles

Synovial fluid 186, 193

Synovial joints 186-7, *188,* 193

Synovial membrane 186

Systems, interrelationship of 4
Systole 14, 15, 17, 19, 21

T

Tartar, *see* Teeth
Taste 162, 177-80; areas of, *179;* buds, 177, *178,* 178-9
Tears, *see* Lacrimal gland
Teeth 55, 56, 188-9
Temperature of body 205
Temporal bone *187*
Temporal lobe *155, 157,* 176, 180
Tendons 164, 182; Achilles', *196*
Testes 98, 109, 115-19, *116, 117, 120, 121; see also* Gonads
Testosterone 93, 109, 118
Tetany 112, 113
Thalamus 154, 155, 158, 159
Theca 126, *127*
Thighs, *see* Femur
Thoracic cage 185, 186, *191,* 191
Thoracolumbar chain 149
Thorax *47*
Throat, *see* Pharynx
Thrombin 32, 33
Thrombocytes, *see* Platelets
Thrombokinase 32
Thumb bone 187, 193
Thyroid cartilage 43
Thyroid gland 14, 44, 67, 82, 91, 98, 110-12, *111, 112*
Thyroid hormone 91, 112
Thyrotrophin 101, 111
Thyroxine 14, 112
Tibia 194

Tissue: types of 2, 3, 8; regeneration of, 10; fibro-fatty, *39;* subcutaneous connective, *202,* 206
Toes 194
Tongue *42, 43,* 55, 56, 58, 162, 178, *179,* 195
Tonsillar region 178
Touch 154, 159, 161, 164
Trachea 39, *42, 43,* 43-5, *46, 111, 113*
Tracts: motor 147, 152; nerve, 146; sensory, 147, 152, 153, 162
Transverse colon *63; see also* Large intestine
Transverse process ... *190,* 190
Triceps *197,* 197, *198,* 198, *199,* 199
Tricuspid valve 12, 14, 16
Trigeminal (5th cranial) nerve 161
Trochlear (4th cranial) nerve, 161, 166
Trophoblasts 134
Trypsin 67
Tubule, nephron 82
Tumors 130, 185
Tunica vaginalis 115
Tympanic membrane *173,* 173, *174,* 174, 175
Tyrosine 203

U

Ulcer: duodenal, 61; peptic, 148; stomach, 60
Ulna 186, 193
Umbilical artery 134
Umbilical cord *135, 138,* 141

Umbilical vein 134
Universal donor, *see* Blood groups
Upper jaw, *see* Maxilla
Upper respiratory system 39-47
Urea, 26, 33, 93; nitrogen, 26
Ureters *84, 85,* 85
Urethra *84, 85,* 86, *87;* female, 86, 131, *131;* male, 86, *120,* 120, *121,* 122, 123
Uric acid 33
Urinary bladder *84, 85, 85,* 87; female, 139; male, *120, 121,* 122
Urinary passages 85-88, 148
Urination, infant 88
Urine 26, 77, 78, 80, 83, 84, 88, 120, 134
Uterus 86, 124, 125, *125,* 128, 129-30, 132, *133, 135,* 137, *138,* 142
Utricle 177
Uvula 56

V

Vagina 86, *125,* 129, 130, *131,* 132, *133,* 141, 142
Vagus (10th cranial) nerve 13, 154
Vas deferens *117,* 119, *120, 121*
Veins *21,* 32, *see also* Blood, Circulatory system
Venous blood, *see* Blood, Circulatory system
Venous trunks 14
Ventricle 12-14, 18, 21; of brain, 150
Vernix 141

Vertebrae 185, *190;* cervical, 189; lumbar, 189; thoracic, 189
Vestibular (8th cranial) nerve, 162, *175,* 175, 176
Villi 64, 68, 69, 134
Vision, *see* Sight
Visual receptive center *157*
Vitamins: A, 75, 76; B-complex, 61, 70, 75; C, 71; D, 69, 75, 76, 185; K, 32, 70, 75, 76
Vitreous fluid 167
Vocal cords *42,* 43, 56, 162
Voice 43
Voluntary motion 156, 158
Voluntary muscles 195
Vomiting 61, 97
Vulva 130-31, *131*
Vulvovaginal gland *125*

W

Water: absorption, 69; in bile, 76; in extracellular fluid, 97; elimination, 206; metabolism, 37, 95-7; in skeletal muscle, 200
Wax, ear 173
White blood cells *28,* 29-30
White matter, *see* Brain, Spinal cord, Cerebral cortex
Worms, *see* Parasites
Wrist, *see* Arm

Y

Yolk sac 135-6

Z

Zygomatic bone *187*

Date Due

Date Due			
Feb 21 57			
Apr 25 57			